This issue of *Ploughshares* is dedicated to

DANIEL AARON
(1912-2016)

Longtime friend, consultant,
and former *Ploughshares* Trustee,
who presided over our formal affiliation
with Emerson College in 1989.

⚏PLOUGHSHARES

Summer 2016 • Vol. 42, No. 2

GUEST EDITORS
Claire Messud & James Wood

EDITOR-IN-CHIEF
Ladette Randolph

MANAGING EDITOR
Ellen Duffer

FICTION EDITOR	POETRY EDITOR
Ladette Randolph	John Skoyles

PRODUCTION MANAGER	BUSINESS & CIRC. MANAGER
Allison Trujillo	David Weinstein

SENIOR EDITORIAL ASSISTANT	MARKETING ASSOCIATE
Michelle Betters	Erin Jones

EDITORIAL ASSISTANT	SENIOR READERS
Belinda Huang	Sarah Banse, Nora Caplan-Bricker,
DIGITAL PUBL. ASSISTANT	Karen Lonzo, John Taylor,
Jessica Arnold	& David Weinstein

COPY EDITOR	ePUBLISHING CONSULTANT
Carol Farash	John Rodzvilla

ASSOCIATE BLOG EDITOR
Amelia Hassani

INTERNS
Sarah Duffett, Kit Haggard, Samantha Harton,
Rebecca Rozenberg, Daniela Serrano, & Isabel Westcott

READERS
Emily Avery-Miller | Jana Lee Balish | Matt Broderick | Susannah Clark
Stephanie Cohen | Lindsay D'Andrea | Zachary Doss | Kristine Greive
Anne James | Autumn McClintock | Sydney Post | June Rockefeller
Joseph Santaella | Michael Schrimper | Charlotte Seley | Angela Siew
Jordan Stillman | Ross Wagenhofer

ADVISORY BOARD
DeWitt Henry | Alice Hoffman | Jill Ellen Karp | Ann Leary
Pam Painter | Tom Perrotta | Janet Silver | Marillyn Zacharis

Ploughshares, a journal of new writing, is guest-edited serially by prominent writers who explore different personal visions, aesthetics, and literary circles. *Ploughshares* is published in April, July, and January at Emerson College: 120 Boylston Street, Boston, MA 02116-4624. Telephone: (617) 824-3757. Web address: pshares.org. E-mail: pshares@pshares.org.

Subscriptions (ISSN 0048-4474): $35 for one year (3 issues and 1 Solos *Omnibus*), $55 for two years (6 issues and 2 Solos *Omnibuses*), and $70 for three years (9 issues and 3 Solos *Omnibuses*); $50 a year for institutions. Add $35 a year for international postage ($15 for Canada and Mexico).

Upcoming: Solos *Omnibus Volume 4* will be published in October 2016. Winter 2016-17, a staff-edited poetry and prose issue, will be published in January 2017. Spring 2017, a poetry and prose issue edited by Jennifer Haigh, will be published in April 2017. Summer 2017, a fiction issue edited by Stewart O'Nan, will be published in July 2017.

Submissions: The regular reading period is from June 1 to January 15 (postmark and online dates). All submissions sent from January 16 to May 31 will be returned unread. From March 1 to May 15, we also read for our Emerging Writer's Contest. Please see page 154 for editorial and submission policies, or visit our website: pshares.org/submit.

Back-issue, classroom-adoption, and bulk orders may be placed directly through Ploughshares. *Ploughshares* is also available as full-text products from EBSCO, H.W. Wilson, JSTOR, ProQuest, and the Gale Group, and indexed in M.L.A. Bibliography, Humanities International Index, and Book Review Index. The views and opinions expressed in this journal are solely those of the authors. All rights for individual works revert to the authors upon publication. Ploughshares receives support from the National Endowment for the Arts and the Massachusetts Cultural Council.

Retail distribution by Ingram Periodicals, Media Solutions, Ubiquity, and Disticor Direct in Canada. Printed in the U.S.A. by The Journeyman Press.

Peter Bichsel, "Telling Stories About One's Life", "Shall I Translate It For You?" © Suhrkamp Verlag Berlin.

© 2016 by Emerson College.   ISBN 978-1-62608-052-2
ISSN 0048-4474

HONORIFIC

PLOUGHSHARES PATRONS

This nonprofit publication would not be possible without the support of our readers and the generosity of the following individuals and organizations.

CONTENTS

Summer 2016

CLAIRE MESSUD & JAMES WOOD
Introduction

It's thought that when Cervantes embarked on *Don Quixote*, he intended to write a short novel. Henry James' short stories had a way of growing into novellas and novels, a fate he fondly cursed. With Chekhov, it was the other way round: life was too short for the novel. (Though perhaps just long enough for a play.) Lydia Davis, who has written one novel and many very short stories, has said that she wrote her only novel because the material needed the extra space: "the subject was there first, and it required a novel."

Perhaps like water finding its level, form eventually finds its own form, and there is very little a writer can do about it? We like the idea that form cannot be imposed, but is fluid and natural, improvised and up for grabs; that hiding inside each genre is the ghost of another form—the essay always about to become a fiction, the novella dreaming of being even briefer than it already is, the short story espying its larger cousin on the horizon. And in a time when prose writing is enjoying an exciting moment of liberation—when fiction and fact, convention and experiment, rules and disobedience, are productively commingling— we are delighted to have been asked to guest-edit this forty-fifth anniversary issue of *Ploughshares*.

Deliberately, we have followed no particular formal criteria— we've just indulged our own agnostic enthusiasm, always excited and always unsure about what exactly fiction is and claims to be. You'll find here, side by side, stories of only one sentence and long stories that are in the process of becoming novels; works of traditional realist fiction alongside fabulists, aphorists, and experimentalists. There is continuous stream of consciousness, and its apparent opposite, the mere fragment; realism and its supposed enemy, allegory. No matter its form, we sought to include fiction that is vivid, vital, and urgent.

If there is an emphasis, it is to bring to *Ploughshares* an internationalism of voice and material, to suit a reality that is at once local and increasingly global and complex.

So we have chosen eminent writers from Algeria (Kamel Daoud), Bulgaria (Georgi Gospodinov), and Switzerland (Peter Bichsel); rising talents from Norway (Gunnhild Øyehaug), Australia (Cate Kennedy), and the UK (Carys Davies). We include fictions by the exhilarating contemporary American writers Viet Thanh Nguyen (whose first novel, *The Sympathizer*, won the Pulitzer Prize earlier this year), and Amity Gaige. The endlessly innovative English poet and dramatist Glyn Maxwell has contributed two fantastical literary imaginings, in which John Keats and John Clare live again, seen reading their work to contemporary audiences. And we are publishing four new stories— delicate as clouds, brief as a change of weather—by our living master of the very short form, Lydia Davis, along with Davis' translations of two pieces by the brilliantly intriguing Swiss writer Peter Bichsel, who is not yet sufficiently recognized in the English-speaking world.

An issue like this is a gibbous moon, which presents only an illuminated portion of its available wealth. We're sad that so much superb fiction has had to be passed over—left, as it were, for now, in the editorial shadow. But we're deeply excited about the striking collection of writers and fictions that we've assembled here, and hope you'll enjoy each singular and memorable contribution.

PETER BICHSEL
Shall I Translate it for You?

Translated by Lydia Davis

Egon is no longer with us, we have buried him—we, a little band
of people. Egon was my friend, and he was my reader. I knew him
a long time and really from a distance, one of many in the bar, and
he burdened people with tricky questions, he could really speak only
in riddles, and when he spoke, he was drunk—because, when he was
not, and he often was not, then he was shy and did not speak. When
I still knew him only superficially, I would not have believed that he
could read, and he surprised me one day with a quotation from my
"Jahreszeiten," and he wanted to find out from me which page of the
book it was on, and became truly angry because I did not know—and
later it turned out that he really had read everything by me. There
would be a lot to tell about him—stories which, back when they were
real, could be quite vile, and now, in one's memory of him, have turned
into stories both funny and sad. If I were to write them down here, they
would give a false impression of him, so I will leave it be. But we told
one another the stories after the burial. They can only be told orally,
they need human voices as signs of the affection in memory. Egon was
a shrewd, cultured person, a formerly successful professional, a former
soccer player, a former referee—in all of them, a former-, and he had
left all that behind and was now only Egon—a unique person, one with
idiosyncrasies and singularities. He would announce himself that way
when he phoned me: "This is the unique person."

Actually, his name was not Egon. That was his nickname. A woman
who was the proprietor of a tavern had called him that, and soon
everyone knew him only by that name. It was a title, so to speak, an
honorary title—the Originals, the Unique, have nicknames. There may
have been others who were really named Egon, but only he was Egon.

The woman who had hung that name on him, as it happened, was
an old Italian and unlike Egon not shy, but also unique and exceptional.
She was really what people mean by an Original, and everyone who

knew her called her Mama or even, Swiss-style, "Mutti," including, indeed, those who did not use the informal "du" with her. Her bar was her kingdom in the real sense, namely a dictatorship. Mama was resolute and definite about what was fair and proper. To that end, she also made use of a stick that stood behind the stove—in jest, true, but still soundly striking. When a woman I knew happened to come in one day, an old acquaintance, and kissed me in greeting, I knew what I might expect: I came in the next day, and Mama took the stick from behind the stove and laid into me—it really hurt a little bit. But people loved Mama, and people were proud of being noticed by her. And she loved everyone— except the southern Italians, and for her the South began to the south of Milan and Turin. She herself came from the Piedmont, and what people said was that as a young girl she had been sent to Solothurn in order to marry a substantially older man who came originally from the same village, was a poultry dealer in the region, and whose wife had died—he needed a new one. And first, she and her husband sold "Jänner," which was what she called the chickens, and one had to learn, by listening to her, her defiant notion of Swiss German. I don't know if she could read and write. In any case, I often wrote letters and postcards for her, and when I pushed them over to her to sign, she would say: "No, you must write 'Lisa'—otherwise it won't be the same handwriting." If I had to describe a typical Solothurn woman, I would choose Mama—a forceful, determined woman who had struggled to win a position for herself in society and really was a conventional, often narrow-minded woman, but with heart and wit—a Swiss through and through, who remained a proud Italian through and through.

But what was it I wanted to tell? Oh, yes, about Egon: When I encountered him one time, he had a set of instructions for something in front of him and said: "I can't read this, it's in English," and I said: "Shall I translate it for you?" "No, for the love of God," he said, "then it wouldn't be English anymore."

PETER BICHSEL

Telling Stories about One's Life

Translated by Lydia Davis

When he starts telling stories, people gradually leave the table or turn away and talk about something else, and generally I'm the one who then has the bad luck to be obliged to listen to him. Someone must listen to him, after all, and he is a friendly man and a quiet and thoughtful one, and he doesn't complain about anything or anyone. He talks very slowly and comfortably, as though he had learned it from his grandfather sitting by the fireside. He tells how they used to steal apples from the neighbor and where the neighbor's house stood and what his name was—"No, that wasn't his name, Baumann was the one on the other side"—and at the end of the telling, it was nothing more than that they had stolen apples. They weren't even caught; they weren't even punished.

He is a frightfully honest storyteller and a terrible bore. I can hardly bear to listen to him. And when he finally comes to the end, then it soon continues: "Two years later—well, not exactly two years, it was in April—we wanted to go over Gotthard Pass on our bikes—well, one of them wasn't a full year older than me—no, that one, the one whose birthday was in November, was his brother, Paul—and who had any money back then and..."

I pay for my beer, take my leave—a really urgent appointment.

He is unbearable, a frightfully bad storyteller. But a lovable man, a former official civil servant, retired for years. He has lived in this town for a long time by now and still doesn't fit in here, and his farmboy background is in the end the only thing that has remained to him.

Almost nothing has happened in his life but exactly the same things that have happened to others: stealing apples and riding bicycles and playing soccer and a little poverty and a little good fortune with the teacher and a little bad luck with the children, and always only a little of everything. As a civil servant he was also only a little authoritarian, and he was also even a little beloved.

I am ashamed each time when I can't manage to listen to the bore.

I never manage it. Yet he, too—now that he will soon be eighty—has a right to a biography, a right to have lived a life, even if almost nothing at all spectacular happened in it. He lived, after all, as we all have not yet lived—and that, too, is something. And if there are still apples today, there were completely different apples back then. They recall the little kid of 1920, shortly after the First World War, back then, when we all were not yet alive. Yes, he truly has almost nothing to tell. But the right to a life, a completely lived life—this he has. It would really be nice if we could listen to each other's boring stories.

For example, I would then tell the following story: "This must have been about 1937, I was two or three years old, I went with my mother into Lucerne, into the town, and at the corner by a large house—I still know where it is, today—my mother met a woman and talked with her for a long time. She was wearing a white dress and had a white poodle, and I became annoyed with her, because I did not want my mother to talk to her, and I pulled on her skirt the whole time and raged. And a boxwood hedge also grew there, and I tore little leaves off the shrub and wrapped them over my fingertips."

That is the story, a boring story without any point, without suspense. It is not at all worth telling. But for a long time now I have wanted to tell it. Now I have done it. Now it is you, dear reader, whom I have deceived, bored, and exploited.

But it had to be told, some day, because it is the first story of my life, the first I remember. It was back then, by the boxwood shrub—so it seems to me—that I awoke to my life. Ever since that story, I have been a person, and if I had written "wrapped the little leaves over my little fingertips," then I would have been lying. No, they were real fingers, the same ones that I have today, and it was a real anger, the same that I have today, and I was a real companion to my mother. And I have the feeling that I was exactly the same back then as I still am today, and that the feeling of anger inside me has not changed at all. This is my most important story, because it is the first story of my life.

But one can't tell it, because it is boring. I remembered it, because I am seeing a granddaughter grow up and seeing her wake up and seeing how she is discovering her fingers and her world. And that is very exciting, above all for her. To discover life—that is really life.

Odd, that one really can't tell it and that anyone who tries to, makes himself ridiculous.

CHAUNA CRAIG

Hidden in Plain Sight: A Companion Reference to Threats, Real and Imagined, as Configured in Late Twentieth-Century Christian America

Ace in the Hole

1. The first Minuteman Missile—America's first solid fuel, fully automated, push-button missile and John F. Kennedy's secret weapon against the Soviets during the Cuban Missile Crisis—was buried in Alpha Six silo, forty miles southeast of my hometown. It took only thirty-two seconds to launch. In 1962, when Khrushchev's threats escalated, Air Command overrode the usual safety procedures requiring four separate approvals from two different command centers to release a missile. Only one command center was actually finished, and rules are always suspended in a crisis. See *Great Falls, Montana, Malmstrom Air Force Base*, and *Minuteman Missile*.

2. The unregistered junk gun my father bought from a junior-high guidance counselor "just in case" and hid in a box in our attic. See also *Saturday Night Special*.

American Redoubt

With origins in the military concept of "redoubt," which means a safe or protected enclave, this describes the region in the American West recommended as a refuge for Christians in the coming end times. The American Redoubt consists of eastern Washington and Oregon, Idaho, Wyoming, and Montana, an ideal hideaway due to its sparse population, libertarian ideals, and landscape abundant with natural resources, like water and game. Proponents have observed, however, that Christians moving to the American Redoubt would be wise to remain west of missile bases, due to the probability of nuclear fallout. See also *Malmstrom Air Force Base*.

American Doubt and Redoubt are awaiting apocalypse. Doubt is annihilated. Who is left?

Antichrist
The opposite of Christ, and thus the opposite of sacrifice and salvation. An ungodly beast whose intention is to enslave us all, the Antichrist can take any form, including that of the Pope, Communist world leaders, and/or Democrats.

My ex-husband liked to tell his children, my stepchildren, that he was 666 years old. We lived in the Bible Belt then, and the kids gleefully shared this detail with their classmates and teachers. When I suggested that claiming to be the Antichrist was no way to make friends, he said I never could take a joke.

My own children recently told me that their father claims to be 666 years old. I see no reason to argue.

See *Armageddon* and *Revelation (Book of)*.

Armageddon
The final battle between good and evil, for which the signs and indicators are abundant if you know where to look. All of my childhood was an education in where to look. See *Eschatology*.

Cabin in the Middle of Nowhere
Before I was born, my grandfather bought a primitive log cabin in a canyon in the middle of Meagher County, Montana. Single room, sleeping porch, outhouse. It was the summer weekend escape of my childhood. Over the years, he added a well and a root cellar "just in case." The only thing I remember anyone keeping in that root cellar was a six-pack of bottled Coca-Cola in 1985 when rumors of a new formula felt like the end of the world.

See *Armageddon, Iodine-131* and *Y2K*. See also *Kaczynski, Theodore*.

The Day After (1983)
A made-for-television movie dramatizing the effects of nuclear war on a town in Kansas and starring Jason Robards and John Lithgow. ABC drew a record 100 million viewers, and the horror of this imagined event was so potentially traumatizing that a free counseling hotline was available.

Lawrence, Kansas, was chosen as the setting for *The Day After* because the 150 Minuteman missiles nearby made the town a "realistic" target. My mother comforted us with this thought: we lived near more missiles than that and would never suffer radiation sickness. We would be annihilated.

Eschatology
The study of end times and all the signs and wonders surrounding them.

Freemen, Montana
On a ranch in southeastern Montana, more properly known as the Middle of Nowhere, a group of people calling themselves "Freemen" gained national attention when one of their leaders declared in the spring of 1995 a holy war of God's laws versus man's laws. The Freemen didn't believe in the government's right to govern and had stopped paying taxes, set up their own court, and even printed their own checks, defrauding banks of thousands of dollars. As they grew more threatening to their peaceful, government-abiding neighbors, the FBI was called. The Freemen barricaded themselves at the ranch, and an eighty-one-day standoff commenced. It ended peacefully with just a few Freemen losing their freedom. The FBI had learned patience by then. See *Ruby Ridge* and *Waco*.

"Going Out in the Field"
How locals described the military drills, often lasting five days or longer, of Air Force missile technicians and security teams, who drove armor-plated Humvees along the highways and gravel roads to any of the two hundred missile silos buried on the plains. To be a local girl with a boyfriend "out in the field" was a marker of social prestige, but only among other local girls looking to marry a "jetter" who might transfer somewhere more exotic than our hometown. See *Great Falls, Montana*.

Great Falls, Montana
1. A city on the northern Great Plains of Montana, population near fifty-nine thousand. Its main industries are hydroelectric power, produced by three dams on the Missouri River, and military power, established by the number of Minuteman missiles still on alert status. There are five waterfalls in and around the city, one of which is now submerged under the reservoir above Rainbow Dam. Also, there are around two hundred missile silos in a hundred-mile radius, all submerged in the soil, many of which are still active, hidden in plain sight.
2. A city I hate for how it defines me.
3. A city I love for how it defines me.

How to Purchase a Missile Base

It's true, you really can buy one. The government had to do something with all those empty silos and abandoned bunkers. Private companies sell repurposed sites in remote areas like Pine Bluff, Wyoming, former site of the Atlas E missile silo. Now the site features an above-ground home already connected to the underground bunker. For around 3 million dollars, you can own a secure place to hide when the end draws near. If you don't have that much money, for $29.95 you can purchase a DVD and take a virtual tour of someone else's survival plan.

Iodine-131

Above-ground testing of nuclear bombs in the deserts of Nevada resulted in radioactive particles, also known as fallout, spreading through much of the West in the 1950s. Fifteen of the twenty-five counties in the US with the highest per-capita dose of radioactive Iodine-131 are in Montana. Meagher County, site of our family cabin, takes top honors for the greatest concentration. Although Iodine-131 decays rapidly, its cycle of contamination circulates from pasture clover to cows to milk and into the human body, where the thyroid absorbs it. Thyroid cancer is highly curable and rather rare. All the radioactive particles had broken down by the time I chased grasshoppers in the meadows, and I've never cared for milk. And so fallout fell out of my mind.

Kaczynski, Theodore

Also known as the Unabomber. He hid out in a cabin in the middle of nowhere in Montana because he knew it was a good place to hide. And it was, for twenty-four years.

Malmstrom Air Force Base

Home of the 341st Missile Wing Command. Originally called East Base for its location on the sunrise side of Great Falls across the bypass from my childhood home, it was renamed for a beloved commander, Colonel Einar Axel Malmstrom, who died in a plane crash. One of my jetter boyfriends told me he got his orders and thought he was headed to Germany. "But no," he said, still sounding disappointed, "it was only Montana."

The 341st has been the site of active intercontinental ballistic missiles since 1961. Its stated mission includes this line: "Deter, Assure…and Kill Bad Guys." See *Ace in the Hole.*

Minuteman Missile

An intercontinental ballistic missile (ICBM) with a maximum range of 8000 miles, developed in the 1960s and now the only remaining land-based ICBM in service in the United States. The missile featured warheads with 1.2 megatons: the explosive power of over a million tons of TNT. A single Minuteman missile contains one-third the power of *all* the bombs exploded in World War II, including those two dropped on Japan. One missile can obliterate an area of 80 square miles and all the human DNA in it. I grew up surrounded by a couple hundred of those missiles. Ground zero indeed.

Paranoia

Just because you're paranoid doesn't mean the Soviets aren't out to get you. There was, my mother claimed, a Communist behind every McDonald's. (She was joking, I think.)

Once, when I was a teenager, my mother mentioned she'd secretly moved my father's gun because she "[did]n't trust what he might do." When I asked about its new location, afraid of stumbling on it while rummaging in the basement utility room, she paused, her eyes narrowing slightly. Then she said she didn't trust me either. She might have been joking, but I never did learn where that gun was hidden.

Prophet, Elizabeth Clare

Cofounder and leader of the Church Universal and Triumphant, which relocated in 1986 from California to a ranch purchased from Malcolm Forbes in southwestern Montana's Paradise Valley. I was in college in Bozeman in the early 1990s, when the church (or cult, depending on who was writing that week's letter to the editor), began building bomb shelters and purchasing .50 caliber semiautomatic Barretts under false names. Call it a church, call it a cult, CUT moved to Montana, expecting it was a good place to hide. When the Soviet bombs never rained down as their leader had predicted, they called it the power of prayer. Then, to escape bad publicity, they revamped CUT as The Summit Lighthouse, describing it as "a non-profit organization." Call that a makeover.

Rapture

In popular parlance, this refers to extreme, transcendent joy. In popular culture, it's a song performed by the band Blondie in which Debbie

Harry raps lyrics about Martians eating cars—an apocalyptic moment if ever I've heard one.

In Biblical usage, this is the much anticipated event in which all Christian believers are airlifted to heaven, saved from the suffering at the end of times. If I were to be rescued, why, I wondered, did I need to worry so much about the End? See *Armageddon, Eschatology,* and *Revelation (Book of).*

Revelation (Book of)

The last book of the Bible. Many people mistakenly add an 's' to the name of this book, but there is only one big reveal: the end of the world will be a bloody, scary disaster that you will only survive if you become a Christian *now.* Saint John dreamed the apocalypse, Armageddon, the end times, complete with a chimaeric beast, a wanton Whore of Babylon, four horses with four riders, and rivers of blood. Seven heads with seven crowns, seven scepters, seven seals, seven stars. And lots of blood. But no seven dwarves or seven brides for seven brothers or magnificent seven. No, this chapter was better than any movie, and I read it over and over. Did I mention all the blood?

Reagan, Ronald

The fortieth President of the United States (1980–88) for whom I wrote an impassioned essay in ninth grade civics noting that only he could save us from the Soviets and the Democrats. I was never old enough to vote for him, but I wanted to. Over and over. See *Saturday Night Special* and *Silver and Gold.* Especially see *This Narrator Was So Damn Young.*

Ruby Ridge

Just because you're paranoid doesn't mean the US Government isn't out to get you.

Russian Drama, Rules of

According to Chekhov, a gun introduced in the first act of a play must go off by the third act. But this is an essay, and the narrator doesn't even know where the gun is. See *Paranoia.*

There are no suggested rules for when a nuclear bomb should go off. The only rule is that rules are always suspended in a crisis. See *Ace in the Hole.*

Saturday Night Special

The type of low-caliber, inexpensive gun used by John Hinckley, Jr. in his attempt to assassinate President Ronald Reagan in 1981. See *Reagan, Ronald*.

When I was young, I confused this with references to *Saturday Night Live*. But there's nothing funny about cheap handguns. Except that my dad thinks he knows how to use one.

Seneca the Younger

Roman philosopher (c. 4 BC–AD 65) to whom this quotation, which was once the epigraph for this essay, is attributed: "We are more often frightened than hurt; and we suffer more from imagination than from reality."

Accused of joining an assassination plot, Seneca was ordered by Nero to kill himself. As the story goes, Seneca opted for the traditional method of slicing through several veins to bleed out. I'd imagine he suffered a slow, painful, and very real death.

Silver and Gold

1. A seemingly innocuous song sung by Burl Ives in the claymation holiday classic, *Rudolph the Red-Nosed Reindeer*.
2. The currency suggested by survivalists and redoubters in anticipation of the collapse of US paper currency. My parents send me silver commemorative coins for every birthday and Christmas to supplement my retirement fund because they do not trust the government (except the mail delivery service, apparently). The only one I haven't sold is my commemorative Ronald Reagan coin because I'm certain that I can barter it for something as frivolous and delicious as jellybeans.*

This Narrator Was So Damn Young

And sometimes still is.

---

*This is the only verifiable lie in this reference. I have never sold my coins for two reasons: 1) The price of silver has never justified the energy expended to find and trust a dealer and 2) The nagging fear that one of my mother's prophecies might someday come true and I'll need those coins for survival. But now that I've revealed I have a cache of silver coins, I will need to buy a gun for protection, and because I have only silver, it will be a cheap gun. See *Saturday Night Special*.

Waco

Just because you're paranoid doesn't mean the US Government isn't out to get you.

Y2K

My parents believed the hype. They had studied for years all the ways a society, especially a Godless society, could collapse into chaos. They stored fifty-gallon kegs of drinking water in their basement. They bought sleeping bags tested to temperatures below zero. Canned food and a manual opener since the failure of public utilities would render their electric one useless. They warned me to make similar preparations, but I was living then in a small town in Arkansas with a man who claimed to be 666 years old. In that climate my sleeping bag wouldn't need to be blizzard-worthy, and my neighbors, though nosy, were Southern Baptist friendly, sure to share their deer jerky.

I was relieved when nothing happened. And maybe, OK, a little disappointed. I don't know if my parents called it a miracle or an answer to prayer, this unchanged world, but the survival supplies were gone or hidden by my next visit, and I never said anything to them except "Happy New Year."

Y2K and Beyond

With a new century came new terrors. After the Cold War, the War on Terror. After 9/11, my mother was finally justified in her refusal to fly, and now I only see her when I make the effort to bridge all the miles between us.

Sometimes I think Montana is a good place to hide, a home to run back to when I'm feeling overwhelmed. I grew up just blocks from what most of us supposed was a literal safe base. But safety in my childhood was defined not as a sense of security grounded in caring relationships, but as the accumulation of objects meant to defend against unpredictable threats. A concealed gun. Silver coins. Buried warheads. A cabin in the middle of nowhere. A manual can opener chewing its way slowly through tin, revealing beans that might nourish or poison, depending on how long they've been kept in the dark.

KAMEL DAOUD
The Ghost's Preface

Translated by John Cullen

We were in Paradise: there was the fig tree and, over on the right, the apple tree, only half of which I could see through the big French window that opened onto the courtyard; there was moreover a cloud of birds so dense you could imagine it contained an infinite number of species. Beyond the garden wall, I could also see the sky, still cool and blue, and I'd let it absorb me when the Old Man's voice stopped addressing anyone but himself, over the heads of all mankind, as it turned its collective back to him.

I would have liked to own such a house: a place where I'd have nothing to do but give things names, for naming things was my true gift in this country, which was losing the use of its tongues.

An old house, calm as an empty sky, with one door that opened on the world and another on memories, nested inside one another like Russian dolls. Even though I was able to glimpse only a part of the garden, I thought it so beautiful that you could sit under one of its two trees and stop aging. By the seventh day, however, I was bored rigid, and I let the voice recorder on the table serve as an ear while the old-timer chattered on, immortalized by his own long-windedness. I smiled and said to myself—sneering intelligently, as you may imagine—"Because death will surely avoid giving eternity to a man who can't shut up." A pretty phrase. The kind of thing that could be carved into a very old stone or inscribed as the epigraph to some profound book. I promised myself to use it one day, when I would address all mankind in my turn. For the moment, however, I was a ghostwriter—in French, a *nègre*—and like black slaves transported to other lands, I let luxuriant jungles grow lazily in my imagination when my task grew too hard in the sun. I'd think about everything, about nothing, drifting like a kite, listening to the voice of a little imaginary serpent and never to the Old Man's story. It, in any case, could have neither a beginning nor an end, unless you trod on the corpse of the person telling it, or if you fired into his mouth the same bullet he'd fired decades ago, before the country became free and useless. I got so bored that I had all sorts of daydreams: about throwing his garden in his face, giving him his money back, and then regretting it for thousands of years; or about killing him by turning my back on him and leaving him planted there, right in the middle of his eternity, on a stunted throne between two trees. I could also leave the courtyard, eat up all his apples, and insolently scratch my crotch to show him what I thought of his desire to dictate a book he couldn't write or didn't dare write, which I'd decided to do from the start anyway.

For three months, I'd helped the Old Man gather up his fragments, verify them one by one, and rebuild his memory. Even before he started rolling out his musty manuscripts, I'd decided to shirk my task. I would deal with it by creating a clandestine story that would stand in for his and survive it by dwelling in its carcass like a patient worm. Here, too, you may imagine me smiling behind a mask: a worm that would not become the too-predictable butterfly of the proverb but would instead eat the leaves, the fruit, the tree, and then the whole forest, and at the end declare itself God. A strategy fit for a copyist incapable of raising his voice, born into an unfavorable century, wedged between two necessities: to eat, and to put off dying as long as possible.

You'll therefore understand me when I say that the chief reason I'm writing a preface to this book today is that the book itself doesn't exist. Its author never wrote it. Somehow my reading aloud an imaginary transcription fooled an illiterate soldier who helped make this country's history, but who could neither read nor write it, nor even find in it the familiar traces of his name. Then the Old Man asked me for a preface, with an insistence that made me uneasy and provoked bitter anger in my heart: tossing me such a scrap seemed like an act of pity, a bit of charity bestowed on a cripple incapable of bearing arms, one who wrote himself a part in the story only because the real heroes hadn't had sufficient time to buy paper and pens. Our ghostwriter-narrator relationship had barely begun before it came to resemble a struggle of wills. The old-timer—who was paying me for his "very own" book and who asked me every three days to show him the typed pages, which he scrutinized as he might a newborn baby of dubious parentage—began to talk of "his" book, using the gestures of paternity frequent among those who have known orphaned childhoods or chosen the poverty of celibacy. "My book" had replaced "my story" at the exact moment when I myself was beginning to see that fabulous story take written shape in *my* hands. It was a story that owed as much to my own way of writing, to my style, to my mastery of a certain language, as it did to the old fellow's tumultuous and now-shriveled life.

The idea came to me the very first evening, when I was rewinding the first cassette tape to transcribe it onto my computer, minus the old fellow's sniffles and coughs. He hesitated between two languages, one of them from over the sea, the other fallen from heaven and then spread across the desert. I'd received a little advance, which made me decide to cheat and opened my eyes to the obvious: I could write whatever I felt like writing, without fear that the Old Man would notice. I could invent an imaginary book in which nothing more serious would take place than the growling of an empty belly at the memory of a big holiday feast. I decided to use the same cassette for our second meeting and all those to follow, without informing the Old Man, erasing the tape each time and recording over it, as people used to do with old animal hides and papyrus and camels' shoulder blades in the days when sacred books were liable to disappear with the deaths of those who recited them. So it was eternity he wanted? I decided to give him a latrine dug into the desert, all the while swearing that the place would become a Mecca for pilgrims, centuries after his death.

The first week, therefore, I wrote down a bit of what he told me about his father and his origins; as he spoke, he watched his stuffed ancestors file past his nearly blind eyes, one of which, dulled by some illness, fascinated me. Under the nose of a man who was illiterate and unbalanced by his imaginary rifle—which he couldn't lay down although the country had been independent for decades—I started to write the book I'd dreamed about for years. I was like an idle God, hesitant to reveal himself, and hesitant to choose a prophet from among his collection of crackpots, even hesitant to create such a vast ventriloquizing mirror as this world. Every Tuesday, the appointed day for me to show him the most recent batch of printed pages, there he was, on the other side of the table: an aging hero from a war no longer worth anything, putting on display the same stagnant memories that all discharged veterans in this country carry around like a skin disease, with the same fetid grudges, the same chortling about imaginary acts of vengeance, the same settling of scores, and, above all, the same murderous words, which have waited so long for their chance that they just cause laughter today.

I was charged with listening like an entire people to this man's discourse, with writing down his words and correcting them. The old fellow dreamed of a final book like a last victory over the Colonist who hadn't allowed him to go to school in the first place or who had forced him to abandon school and take up arms. He fought alone in a place no one visited, wielding weapons a century old, alone in his own woods, crying out names and truths I was charged with gathering. His was but one story, which although it started out with singing and rifles, could end only with stammering, the fruit of the Independence that had given him victory but no means to recount it, in a country where nothing happened anymore. Worst of all, he felt I should serve as his ghostwriter not because he paid me, but because I myself had a debt to pay off, a debt to *him*, who had offered me this country on a silver platter while blissfully unaware that he'd already eaten more than half of it. "It's because we sacrificed ourselves for your sake that you can be proud of your ability to read and write today," his generation repeated, at length, to mine. So you'll understand why I had to bet on his deterioration and wait for him to croak, or change his mind, or cut his epic down to the essential point: that he had fought in the war and wanted Creation to stop and salute him every time they crossed paths.

From the beginning, with him perched on a mountain he no longer wanted to come down from and me sitting on the other side of the writing table—which in this country will always separate the man who knows how to write from the man who's too old to learn—it was tacitly agreed that I was to consider his story true and swallow it whole. In return, he was to believe my art sufficiently accomplished to recreate every detail of his epic battles, right down to the smallest speck of dust, in the days when the world revolved around him like a young girl offering him her virginity. I knew he was laying it on thick—the only roles he assigned to his former comrades in arms involved dishwashing or couscous preparation or gathering the inferior herbs of the maquis, while he stood up to battalions of Frenchmen—and he knew that I, like many scribes, could write only for money and only as a ghostwriter, a servant, and therefore an invisible man.

As far as that loathsome competition between a loquacious cadaver and a gravedigger, I must say that I shared responsibility equally with my client: there was, on both sides, the beginning of hatred between us. Every Tuesday, when we'd go through the pages I'd printed out, there were the discreet, sterile, and completely mad allusions to the eventual glory that would surround each of us, thanks to this book. The experience of the war had made the author sensitive to the scent of plunder, and he could smell from far off how I was fiddling his words, fudging his meaning and his diction, tinkering with his scene choices and with the dialogues and reflections I put in his mouth. Like a peasant with distrustful eyes, he was suspicious of the false wool on the animal I was trying to sell him—the second, clandestine book, *mine*, which I was slipping in behind his own in order to record my signature, my writing, my own way of seeing the world.

The wily warrior, obliged to count his bones every morning before he could walk, who'd been dead for a long time without knowing it, attempted to cleanse his book of any trace of me by a pretty technique of encirclement: after we'd read the most recent pages together, he attacked me over insignificant details, proposed changes that contradicted what he'd told me the previous day and, above all, wasted my time on descriptions he was going to cut in the final reading, on tedious corrections to dates and encryption games meant to disguise names and places, erasing as he went along the tracks of all footsteps not his own. The old fellow wanted me to be utterly a ghost, without a given name, awaiting the call of his little bell, hardly more visible than a magic orthography machine, barely capable of holding a pen. Those little corrections led to long lessons in history and heroism, the sort of lectures so dear to all this country's war veterans, who have either no descendants or only ones who don't believe in their elders. And I had to serve not only as this wreck's ghostwriter, his mute interlocutor, but also as his son, paid an hourly wage to reestablish a lost filial relationship, to service the heritage machinery. Often, when the Old Man was telling me his story, he'd take on the appearance of a vampire, or a spider, or better yet a completely deboned human being. I became the figure of his essential drama and the image with which he overcame his castration, his impotence, the legendary infertility of his entire generation.

I sensed his panic at the idea that he had to die—really, absolutely, and not from a bullet, but worse: from the sweep of a broom, or the wipe of a cloth, between two pieces of period furniture. Clumsy novelist or shapeless ghost that I was, my story couldn't stand up to his and got itself swallowed up like Jonah, swallowed by a whale with a fantastic digestive tract. I often left our three-hour sessions exhausted, afflicted by violent headaches and certain that I'd been emptied of something more essential than blood, that a dirty animal had made a meal of me. Half of the happiness I felt at gazing upon the garden of that villa, which the Colonist had abandoned, half of my joy in the game of starting over, was spoiled by the obligation to put up with the old fellow, to chew on his story and dodge his spittle. I was reminded of one of the most anxiety-inducing images of my childhood: the image of Sinbad in the *One Thousand and One Nights*, the sailor shipwrecked on an island where he awakens with an old man on his back who refuses to get off. Like all those of my generation, I had always detested war veterans, but until recently I had never known that a strange odor clung to their skin, the smell of their failed death. When you spend time with those people, you always feel as though you're betraying half the country's population. Worse yet, you feel crushed, disabled, reduced to a token role, and in the end dirty on the inside, like a grave.

Somewhere around the third chapter—having written a long, grandiloquent introduction related to the increasingly unreliable story this country's been telling itself since its victory over the Colonist, and after thirty pages about the author's illustrious father—I began to see that poverty was clearly not the only thing at stake in this book. I came to understand that another battle was being fought between me, the invisible little writer, and the Old Man. What was going on wasn't a simple comic interaction, but a scandal in the most naked sense of the word, a fight over the paternity of all the books that have been written in this country and of all the other possible versions of this very book, and especially over the freedom to write it, to give it a name and an author. We often sat in the same living room—its walls still warm from the Colonist's tenure, from his laughter and his harvests—while one of us conjured up rivers the other was paid to drink. Citizens of a free country, we put together our story, the thirty or so pages eternally missing from the biography of this land.

One day, I remembered a saying drummed into my head when I was a schoolboy, a declaration I was obliged to repeat like a recording:

that the story of this country was a book, it was all possible books, and no story could be told without telling this story, which told them all.

Book production and authors, when they really existed, were strictly monitored; they were supposed to toe a line between the gunfire of the famous War of Liberation and the peasant utopia that had always been its goal.

I remember discovering, in my early days, that it was impossible to escape our unique national story. Its infinite repetition repelled me. The explanation of this country's creation was like one from days gone by, when the world was thought to have been born from the egg of some fabulous animal, from the paper tissue of a perspiring God, from a magic sardine, or from some other creature that plunged to the bottom of the sea. The literature I devoured after I read my first crime novel at the age of nine—and I can still remember the sentence that made my precocious sexuality explode: "The woman came toward him, naked, still wet from the tepid water she'd been swimming in"—was my only way to escape the universe of national glory. I later learned that it was impossible to write anything other than the history of that war, or to write anything against it. Facts, dates, and names were nowhere to be found in all the confusion. I was a hapless investigator, on the scene not to discover some truth, but to earn a little extra money on top of my meager salary.

I remember another sentence, which later, after I became a journalist, I found more or less everywhere in the memoirs published in this country: "And so future historians will have to judge…etc." In this country, everybody wrote under the tyranny of an invisible future historian, awaited at the end of the book like a sort of stern messiah, obese from long sitting and incapable of movement, charged with gathering together the various writings and reducing the cosmos to a single preface. It was impossible to write a simple love story, for example, or a story about a memorable encounter or a miraculous catch of fish, without ending up in the violent and terrible library where several million copies of a single book have been assembled, a book everyone claims as his own. My only freedom is to introduce you to this book I didn't write, and to explain to you the reasons why I refrained from writing it.

I experienced the impossibility of writing as though it were just my individual problem, whereas in fact it was a law imposed on all, by all. According to those who lived through the revolution, it chose very early on to murder everyone who could, one day or another, endanger the unique version of the facts, collect divergent testimony, or write books that scorned the war. Speaking in a strangely jubilant tone, the old fellow told me the following story, which could be retold in two pages or in six hundred, as it featured only one soldier, charged with killing an officer who was his compatriot but also a man of letters. Instead of a last cigarette, the officer asked his killer to let him speak to God for the entire night before his execution: "The Murderer is still alive today, living in a town, you know. He's completely paralyzed, and he's paying for his crimes with a living death.

"At the time of the story, his commanders had ordered him to kill ninety-two of his fellow resistance fighters, suspected of preparing a book, of having read one, or simply of being capable of reading one. The Enemy had infiltrated our ranks, and the fear of treachery was everywhere, especially within the groups that had accepted academics and Algerian students fresh out of the Colonist's lycées. The day came when the Murderer was ordered to execute the most pious, most educated, fairest, and noblest man he'd ever known. All the same, he informed this man that he was on the list. You know, my son, the saintly man didn't rebel, didn't try to escape or to dissuade his executioner. He asked only to be allowed to pray until dawn. The Murderer told me he'd waited patiently until sunrise, while his condemned comrade conversed with God as though he were within reach of his hand, laughed with him, wept a little, teased him, told him the story of his own life, revealed his confident bewilderment, and asked for absolute justice at the exact price of the injustice that was being done to him."

The Old Man went on to explain how during that night, the victim had discussed with his God all the atrocities the country had experienced since Independence; he'd negotiated, corrected excesses and insufficiencies, dates and methods, the number of victims and predestined executioners. What a strange auto-da-fé this country commits, burning books before they're written, killing everyone who might one day give birth to a writer, a reader, or a simple, undisciplined storyteller! Following a long tradition, the Old Man couldn't help seeing in me the scribe still capable of betrayal, just as I could not help seeing in him the guilty witness of a vast perjury. The other sorrow—mine alone—was that I'd never been able to write my own book, and that when it was at last within my power to put a story in writing, it wasn't my story, its hero was a liar, and it had to be published under a ridiculous nom de guerre.

After having waited so long, I'd been reduced to rebirth in the form of a cancerous dotard, half of whose words were addressed to the dead and the other half to his own dentures.

And so I'm amusing myself with this improbable ghostwriter's preface, because I am at once the author, the thief, the copyist, the scribe, and the double-crosser of our contract.

In truth, the old fellow was a poor, ugly thing. His sole fortune was his name, which he was going to give to my work. At seventy-two, wasted by a cancer that nibbled on his insides, the Old Man was looking for an ending, a clear-cut epilogue, the conclusion of the extended repartee between him and fame. For me, the Old Man was the accidental father, the paternity that since Independence has reduced this country to a reading room across from a choir room. But the matter was even more complex. Ever since my youth, I'd had the intuition that my country suffered not only from a lack of nourishment and hope, but from an even more terrible affliction: idleness. I was a child of the Independence, born when idleness was at its height, that is, at the moment when all the reasons, all the tricks, all the easy pickings were running out. So it's understandable that, in a way, I never grew up, I just waited patiently to learn the right words and the practice of reflection. None of the novels written since Independence has been anything but the tasteless fruit of idleness, and of the dead's loss of interest in their own eternity. Those books tell no stories, like this preface, and they plunge ahead like lost travelers, increasingly remote and never coming back to tell us news or lies or feed us edible fables. The explanation is that we are a race confined to the boundaries of our own land, regarding the sea as an obstacle, not as half of our own eternity, and moreover turning our back, with unimaginable contempt, on the desert.

Besides, if the dead don't speak, they shouldn't write or tell tales either.

The codger had paced around in his cage without being able to write for so long that his sentences were almost visible inside his cheeks before he opened his mouth. His story could perhaps have become interesting had it led to something other than the expectation of a giant medal. To summarize this imaginary book, therefore, it's enough to say, in a few lines, that the old guy had served in the French army and talked about it like some kind of gigantic day-before-yesterday, suspended like a fabulous garden covered with vineyards and paths, before he took up arms and then seized the rest of the country—single-handedly, as it were. He claimed descent from an old family that itself descended from the Prophet.

At the age of twenty, according to the tale he retold through my servile ghostwriting, he'd been called to duty under the French flag, and had served France on her soil with the astonishment of a native who, wide-eyed, sees his first automobile. Over there, he told me, he became acquainted with enthusiasm, with the zeal that, if disappointed, leads to war and murder. His nationalism came later, like a contagion, right after his return to the country to complete his service in Tlemcen province. There, confined to inaction and fearing he'd fall back to earth if he abandoned his uniform, he sought a way out and found it in the secret revolt of his people against the Colonist. Seven years of war, during which he was imprisoned, tortured, and then freed by his comrades, had made him admirable, but as uninteresting as a number in a poem.

Sometimes I felt remorse as I looked at the Old Man, bending over pages covered with fallacious writing as though over his own life. At such times I would confront in myself the crook I was. The old fellow's story occasionally reeked of falsehood, but the book I claimed to be writing for him was still more false. Still more despicable than his miserable little vanity. I often left the old house, the scene of the story-telling, with the sensation that my pockets were stuffed with stolen objects, and in the evenings the soft white part of the bread I ate had a corpselike taste. I felt guilty, but that never lasted very long. Maybe because I was used to it, or maybe because I figured I shouldn't ruin my life. His wizened face belonged not to a man but to a time, and so I could treat him the way you treat an old clock.

So I stole from the Old Man, emptied out his memory, and filled it up with sand. The undertaking lasted three months, at the end of which I had a text to thrust under his nose, more than two hundred pages, including a portion of this absurd preface. I'd stuffed the whole thing like a farce: there was the story of a long-distance runner who couldn't stop running, the tale of a lunatic airplane manufacturer I'd run into one day, and the first chapters of a novel I'd never been able to finish, about a man who didn't want to leave his apartment before leaving his body. I remember the Old Man, unable to read the words, looking at the pages like someone choosing a book to put on the night table inside his grave, for millennia—inhaling their smell, caressing them. The way he used to do with his weapon in the old days, or the way a God would do with his last, long-awaited sacred Book. He started dreaming right there in front of me, unmoving, his single eye like a broken windowpane. For a moment, I thought he was about to die, but then I made a show of gathering up my things under the pretext of leaving him time to read over the whole manuscript before the final version was printed.

If I persist in writing this preface, it's so that I may record his grotesque, improbable end. When I returned on the following Tuesday to see the Old Man and receive the rest of the money due to me, I was admitted by his eldest son, who informed me of the author's sudden death the previous Wednesday, and expatiated at some length upon what I represented for his father and for the whole family.

Once again, I sat facing the French window that opened onto the little Paradise of the garden. The smell of the crowd that had come to offer their condolences still hung in the living room, along with the Old Man's particular scent. I found it strange to be sitting there and gazing at the son, who bore such a resemblance to his father. I was offered tea and allowed to look at the fig tree, perhaps for the last time. I knew I'd miss the place for millennia and dream of it for centuries: there was no longer any excuse for me to come back here. The son was still talking to me about his father. Whenever I was on the point of yawning, I clamped my mouth shut out of courtesy, and from time to time I even restarted his monologue with hackneyed gestures. I played this game for a long time. I wanted to get the text back before the deceased's descendants discovered my villainy and hanged me or had me shot, as had been done to practically my entire line of forgers ever since the first day of the war.

The son, already old himself, fixed a surprised gaze on me for a moment and then lowered his voice and explained that his father had scrutinized the manuscript for hours on the day before he died and then spent almost all night burning the whole thing. "Nobody dared ask him to stop, no one dared ask why he was doing it." The son was embarrassed, waiting for my reaction. For an instant, I was tempted to get angry, but I quickly realized there would be no point. The book had never been written, and you can read it anywhere in the country.

No one escapes it. Millions of copies rot in the sun, in the cafés, in the schools. You need only look closely or follow the odor of great mustiness to find pages of the volume. The Old Man could die, for there were already thousands of other madmen, raving just like him. Even some who had never participated in the War of Liberation. The book is everywhere, like a God or a giant circle that swallows all the other books and reduces them to scraps of dialogue, punctuation marks, or the titles of stammering chapters.

All it's missing is a Preface.

CARYS DAVIES
The Testimonie of Alyss Teeg

After a weak Trig sed maybee we shud call Gil Semmens, have him Eye-Ball James Elward.

Ma laffd, Semmens?

Trig shiftid in his chare, looking like he wishd he-ud kept his Mouth shut, but it was too layt for that, Ma full of scorn, was alreddy in his fayce—Had Gil Semmens nown how to saive Pa's Poisond Fut? Or Trig's own tatterd Arm? Had Semmens ever, in Six Long and Dust-Layden Summers, come forwud with any useful remidie for Dilly's Hayfever? Did Trig trewly bileeve that such a purson cud help James Elward now in his Currant Pridicamint?

She leend forwud and cuffd Trig across the Hed and said she didnt plan on paying out any Doctors Fees for this one, leest of All three dollars to witniss a Cretin like Semmens lay his eer to James Elward's chest and shyne a tinie lite in his eers and his eyes and ask him a lot of questshins about what hes been eeting and wether he has a payne in his Hed or his Hart or any other Part of his bodie, and give her a round green pil or a worthliss wite powdur in a twyst of paper to sprynkle in James Elwards tee.

Trig bowd his hed, rubbd his eer where Ma had caut it with the flat of her Hand and lookd Sheepish for a wile. It did not prevent him however later on that Afternoon, coming up with a diffrint plan—for Him and Pa to take James Elward hunting. The three of them off in the Wilderniss beyond Larabee Countie—a camp fyre and a deer carcuss strung up from a Lodgepole, the good ion smell of blood, the sound helthie Sleep of the Hunter.

Pa, sitting across from Trig, said he concurd with his eldist Son. The two of them noddid their big simlar heds. I wonderd how far into the wilderniss Pa woud be able to git with his crutch and his one good fut, and how sucsesfull Trig wud be weelding a ryfle with his mashd-up arm, but Ma did not pursew the Matter. She shot Pa a look of Scorn and gave Trig another wack around the Hed, lookd him in the eyes and told him she was weery of his Prattel.

*

He is a tall fayre-haird boy of fifteen, my brother James Elward Teeg, and it is exactlie one month since he announcd to me and Dilly and Ma and Pa and Trig and Delphine that God has made a missteak and he is amending the error now as best he can.

It is exactlie one month since there was, in the wake of this Anouncment, a seene of some cayos in our House—Dilly in tears, Delphine saying, Oh My Lord, that is somthing I was just *not* ecspecting. Trig mute, staaring. Pa getting up out of his chare and nocking James Elward to the ground with the point of his crutch and busting James Elwards lipp.

After that, a breef and gastly Quiet.

Then Delphine, standing there in her droopie shorl, shaking her Hed and saying, Well I gess we dont none of us, never, do we, see The Big Things Coming. Ma, not lisening to a word Delphine had to say—Ma with her chin razed and her hands akimbo, stepping forwud bitween Pa and James Elward and asking Pa in a lo and feersom voyce if he considerd that an intelligent way to proseed, to attack James Elward with his Crutch? To try and beet it out of him?

She is always the smart one, Ma.

Ryte from the begining she seems to have figurd out that this is a serius thing. From the momint James Elward came downstayrs that day with the news that he is Laura Kathrine now and not James Elward any more, she seems to have understood that his transformayshin is by far the worst thing ever to be-fall the Teegs—wors than Pa lossing his fut from the rusted nayle, wors than Trig getting his left arm mangld off in the Thresher, wors than Delphine not getting the money that was expectid to come her way upon the Deth of her Granma over in Pidgin Cove.

In the middle of the Room Ma stood between James Elward and Pa and Pa's blood-spotid crutch with her sholders squard, in her bonie jaw the firm-set look she always gits in the fayce of miss-fortune that seems to say: *We will get thro this. We will. We will Over-Come. I will make sure of it. It will be without the help of my useliss Husband and my feckliss eldist son and his iritating wiyfe and my two young dauters but I will manige it. Yes indeed. Even tho I do not diserve this, even tho I am burdind with work like a weery pack-horse with hardly one harf-secind to call my own to put my feet up or take a puf of my pype, I, Hanna Mary Josefine Elward Teeg, will set my sholder to the weel and sort this out.*

Ma, a Tower of Strenth.

Ma the most practical and resoursful and vigurrous and capabel Persun in the hole of Jefferson—Ma who is on the go all day, every day, from the minit she climes out of bed in the morning til the momint she falls into it at Nyte. Ma the one to do practicly every last thing in this house, every Big thing and every Littel thing. Ma the one to mend the roof and creesote the fens and figur out the acunts. Ma the one to fix Dillys bow in her difficult hair on Carnival Day, Ma the one to chase down Trigs favrit Pig when it gets looss in the Andersons corn, Ma the one to bang down a vast dish of butterd sweed upon the table and demand to know, What in the name of Heven, would the Teegs do without Her?

Over on the other syde of the room Trig was still gorping, and Dilly had started crying agen.

Stop it Dilly, I wissperd. Everything will be alrite. Ma has her Thinking Cap on. Ma will over-come. Ma will discover the thing to do.

The next morning at brekfast nobodie sed anything.

We passd the dishis to eech other and we ate. James Elward sat next to me. He seemd quite composd and he did not look imbarassd. Trig, further down the Tabel, regardid him seecritly the hole time with his Eye-Balls angld and drawn upwids while he kipt his fayce over his playte. Pa ate noisully and when he was done eeting he sat looking at James Elward with his jaw still going from side to side, rithmicly like a Cows, as if he was chewing on something Gristlie and Hard he cudnt swollow. Delphine lookd skywid in her acssepting and unquestshunning way with a sireen smyle on her fayce and I did wonder, looking at her, if she was experincing some privit joy to see Ma wressling with this dificult and unecspectd developmint. Dilly sat looking around at evryone, hardly eeting a thing, looking baffld and miseribbel.

As for Ma herself, she sat up strayt and tall at the end of the tabel in her big Carver Chare with the woodin arms, sometimes looking at James Elward and sometimes not. When brekfast was over and cleerd away I watchd her go out to feed the Pigs and you cud tell she was thinking all the time about James Elward and What To Do.

It was the same that evning after supper, and it was the same evry evning after that for more than a weak. Out there in the Not-Quite-Dark you could see her lipps moving, as if she was muttring furiusly about

Doctors and Hunting and hitting People with crutches—about Pa and Trig and their stupid ideas, and about Delphine shaking her head and torking about how none of us ever seem to see The Big Things Coming, acsepting it all with her slow Delphine shrug; a flat, dry spung, soking up the Wollups of the World.

Harf-way through the secind week I was standing one nyhte at the kitchin window agen, watching. I saw Ma turn the emptie Pig buckit Up-Sidown and give it a wack to nock out any last bits of feed stuck to the bottim. I watchd her check the Pen was closd on the animals and when she came insyde I watchd her do something she hardly ever does—Sit Down.

With all her Chores done for the day—the Floor mopd, the Stove cleend, the new buckel sowd onto Dillys old Shoos, the fire layde, the Pigs fed, the Plaster changd on the horribel Fresh Boyle on Trigs neck, the buter churnd—she sat down and lit her Pype and started pufing away at it while she stard into the Fyre, and the next morning when me and Dilly came down for brekfast, she was still there in her Chare, pufing away.

Without making a noyse I got the Bowls out and cut the bred.

Dilly said, Ma? Can I have some milk?

Ma didnt turn a hair. She was staring into the Cold Fyre. In the erly morning lite, I cud see her eyes glissning. In my hole life I had never seen Ma cry before. He has always been her favrit, James Elward, her Darling Goldin Boy, and sitting there in front of the cooling emburs of the Fyre, she had the look of someone whose Hart was brokn in two and there was Nothing at all now on her mynd but how to Fix It Back Together Agen.

When Dilly askd a secind thyme, could she plees have some milk, Ma's gayze stayd on the Fyre.

Quiet, girl, she sed. Cant you see Im busie?

Here, Dilly, I sed. Ill git your milk. You leeve Ma to do her Thinking.

It was blue, James Elwards Dres. A horribel faydid long-sleevd Thing he-ud procurd from We Know Not Where. On his Hed, on top of his fayre hair, a whyte gorze Cap, like mine and Dillys, kept in place with four Silvery Pins.

One nyhte not long after we found Ma sitting in front of the cold Fyre, he came taping at our Bedroom Door, mine and Dillys.

In he steppd in the horribel blue gown. He must have heard Dillys snufling thro the wall because what he sed was, Hush, Dilly, Dont Cry.

He sat down next to her on the bed and touchd her cheek with the side of his fingur.

His bustid lipp was crustid over and beginning to heel.

Evrything would be allryte, he sed.

He sed it had been a Big Thing coming downstairs that day and showing himself and telling Ma and Pa and Trig and Delphine and me and Dilly, but it was done now and prettie soon he was going to start getting out of the House and going into Jefferson. He just had to get his nerv up a bit more, but prettie soon he wud do it and by the end of the summer when we went back to school evryone would know that he was Laura Kathrine now and not James Elward anymore. He ecspectid to have a Bad Thyme at first, he said. He ecspectid that to begin with Certin Peepel wud laff and make fun of him and wissel and pass vary-us Remarks when he went by that he-ud sooner not heer, but peepel wud git used to it evenshally; evryone in Jefferson wud, and everything wud be alrite after a littel wyle.

Dilly lay in bed with her Hed on the pilow.

What about Pa? she sed.

Pa would git uscd to it, sed James Elward.

What about Trig and Delphine?

Trig would git used to it as well, and Delphine was alreddy used to it.

Dilly sniffd. What about Ma?

Ma wud get used to it also.

You think?

Yes I think.

Reely?

Yes Reely.

And for a few days after that it did seem like James Elward myte be rite.

For a few days we livd in a kind of peecefull Lymbo, a karmish stayte where evrything felt almost alrite agen. Like James Elward pridictid, Trig and even Pa seemd evry day to get a little more used to him being The Way He Was, and Ma, if she was still thinking about how to fix her Brokn Hart, didnt tork about it, and I didnt see her muttring to herself any more as she went about her Hundrid Chores. In the evnings before sundown, she even sat smoking with Pa and Trig and Delphine out on the back step, while me and Dilly playd out in the yard with the skiping rop, and James Elward wud come out too and take one end of the rop and we-ud turn it while Dilly skipt and her Beautifull Tangld Curls bouncd and flopd and she laffd and pantid and when she got too tyred to skipp anymore James Elward wud pick her up and swing her round and throw her into the ayre and catch her agen, and kiss her nose, just like he did before he decidid he wasnt a boy any more, and Dilly wud throw her arms around his neck and call him Laura and say she was Hapy there was no more Shouting or Hitting or torking about going hunting or having Dr. Semmens come and visit us with his big black bag full of powdurs and tonics and sharp, shyney instrumints.

Then one nyte after dinner when James Elward had gone up to his room, Trig spok.

Maybe, he sed, a Witch had put a Spell on James Elward to make him turn himself into a Girl.

Pa lookd up and so did Dilly and Delphine.

Delphine rolld her eyes and kind of laffd. Dilly, who was frytind of witchis, lookd Startld and Scard. Ma pushd back a stray peece of hair that was hanging down in front of her fayce. She liftid the emptie potatoe dish off the tabel.

Don't be a cretin, Trig, she sed. Aint no such thing as witchis.

But Ma seemd to grow thortfull after that. She sed nothing for the hole of the rest of the evning—she cleered everything away to the sink without a word, and when she came back she went to stand over by the harth, leening a littel with one sholdur against the chimmny brest, pufing on her Pype and looking into the fyre, and it was like you could see some slow and carfull activitie going on inside her Hed—all the tinie toothd Coggs that linkd her Quick Spritely Brayne to her Big Pumping Hart and her long synewey Arms, all of them going round and round and round while she was thinking about what Trig had sed.

In bed that nite Dilly sed, Alyss? Was there ever a Witch here in Jefferson, or any other Plaice in Larabee Countie?

No Dilly. Of cors not.

Dilly noddid, but she lookd at me, even so, with big frytind eyes.

I put my hands on both her sholdurs and lookd into her fayce. You herd Ma, Dill. Aint no Such Thing as witchis.

Dilly noddid solemlie. So Trig cudnt be rite?

No, Dilly, he cud not.

And then, because she still lookd so miseribel and afrayd and it seemd importint to cheer her up, I startid tickling her and asking her, when cud she *ever* rimember Trig being Rite about anything? and Dilly squeeld then, under the tickling, and chortld and laffd and sed, Never, o never, o stop, Alyss, stop tickling me, and after that she cudnt speek any more, she was just laffing, laffing, laffing.

I kept thinking though, how thortfull Ma had been earlier, and when Dilly was asleep I went downstairs and found Ma still leening against the chimmny brest, still pufing at her pype. Pa and Trig and Delphine had takin themselvs off out onto the porch. She was still ruminating, you cud tell. I wantid to ask her what she was thinking, but I thort if I did she-ud git cross and tell me to shut up and say I was getting on her nervs even more than Delphine. So I didnt say anything. I stood there in my nytegown and in the end she was the one who spok.

What is it, girl? What do you want? and I said I was just wondring what idea it was she was away there nursing in her Hed wile she sat pufing on her pype.

Ma noddid.

She took another deep pull on the pype and blew off the smok and lookd at me and then back at the fyre and sed, The onlie one I got, girl.

She is not an unappeeling woman, Ma.

Bone-ee in the fayce with thin wispy hair but tall and shapelie with a fine busum and beautifull Toes.

Yesterday after brekfast when all the others had got up from the tabel, she told me and Dilly she was going upstairs to get Dressd and since she alreddy was Dressd, we followd her.

From the doorway we watchd her role a payre of cleen stockings up over her baare legs and take the carneleean Lipp Color she never wares but keeps in a Goldin Cartouche in a box on her dresser from her wedding day and paint her mouth with it, and when Dilly askd her, where was she going looking so Pretty she sed, Never you mind, girl.

She was gone most of the day and harf the evning and when she came back the carneleean lipp Color was worn away and she lookd tyred but also peecefull, as if she-ud done whatever it was she needed to do—as if she-ud discoverd at last the rite way to set her sholdur to the weel and sort things out.

It is a tall, wyde bilding, the Jefferson corthouse. Whyte and woodin, it sits hi on a square paved Rise at the far end of town.

The doors were opin when we arrivd and inside the baylifs were there, and the two lawyurs, Mr Hill and Mr Summerton—Judge Limbaugh just entering from a door in the far left corner that Trig wissperd in my eer leeds rite into his own privit sitting room.

He is an old man, Judge Limbaugh, dressd in a rustid black rob, with a long blue-lippd fayce and yellow hair.

He is the closist thing we have in Jefferson, Ma told us last nyte, to a King.

He does what he likes, she sed. He is nown for it. Anything in Jefferson, he is the one to decide how it will go.

I tryed not to look at him. It was awfull to think of his old blue lips on top of Ma's carneleean ones, which was how I imagind it—the two of them in his privit sitting room, her tuff ditermind smyle, her strong legs in their cleen stockings, her short playne way of puting things into speech. *Here I am, and here is what I need in Exschange.* Ma knowing how to make a bargin happin.

Last night after she came home and James Elward had gone up to his room and Dilly was in bed asleep, she calld the rest of us together, and told us how it was going to be today. When we got to the corthouse there would be some baylifs, she sed, and Judge Limbaugh, and two lawyurs, Mr Hill and Mr Summerton.

Mr Hill was the Jefferson Prosecutur, she sed, and Mr Summertons job it would be to argue against Mr Hill.

Pa noddid. If he mindid about Ma going to see Judge Limbaugh with her stockingd legs and her payntid lipps, he didnt say So. He sat with his crutch proppd against his chare and his hands on his nees and I had the impreshun Ma had alredy gone over things with him. Trig liftid his Big Slow Hed. Why did we need the secind lawyur sticking his oar in and puting a diffrint spin on things? Couldnt we just keep with the grand old judge and the Prosecutur? Wouldnt that be enuf?

Ma made a tssking sound between her teeth and cuffd him around the tempel with the heel of her hand. Although she seemd on the hole to be very calm, she was, as on many and multipel other ocasions, weery of his stupid questshins.

No we cannot, Trig.

Why not?

Because the cort's the cort and everything has to be done rite and there always has to be two lawyurs.

Trig rubbd the sore patch at his tempel. And a judge?

And a judge, yes.

Which was why, sed Ma, no one needid to worrie about there being a secind lawyur, because that was all squard away with Judge Limbaugh. Judge Limbaugh had this secind lawyur in his pockit, same as he had the prosecutur in there too. Like I sed, sed Ma, the judge does what he likes. Anything in Jefferson, he is the one to descide how it will go.

Delphine sed she wasnt sure, it didnt seem rite to her, maybe we should leeve things the way they were, let it all be.

Trig sed No, it would be alrite. Ma had it coverd.

Delphine rung her ropie Hands. What exactly did Ma plan on saying to James Elward? she wantid to know. To Dilly? What wud we tell them? Would we say that we were in no Dout? And being in no Dout, would we say we had no Choyce? Would we say that we had no Dout and the only thing we cud do now was let the cort take care of it? Is that what we would say to James Elward and to Dilly? Wudnt they run away, the two of them, if we told them why it was we all had to go along to the corthouse and stand before the judge?

In my hole life I had never herd Delphine string so many words together in one go.

Ma took a breth, like someone having to be pashunt and understanding with a very stupid persun.

We will say it is for a diffrint reason we have to go, Delphine, she sed. An ordnarie thing like the squabbel with the Andersons over Trig's pig devouring their corn.

Delphine chewd her lipp—what if James Elward sed he preferd to stay home? What if he sed he was not yet reddy to leave the house and show his transformashin to the World?

In a hard flat voyce Ma sed she wud talk to James Elward—suggest to him that there was no thyme like the present to step outside and mingel agen with other foke.

Delphine stood silint but Trig took her hand and pattid it, and that seemd to sooth Her.

It was Judge Limbaugh who began things when we got to the cortroom, by asking my brother James Elward in a slow and lytlie suthern drawl, how he was today.

James Elward, in his duskie blue frock and his wite gorze cap, blushd and said he was fyne. If he was surprysd to be adressd by the judge, he did not seem unduly alarmd. Doutless he was ecspecting a digree of attenshin, this being his first outing into town, and now that he had it, he seemd to want to rise to the ocashin. If he-ud been nervus about coming out into the World, he seemd more confident now. Alreddy on our walk thro town to the corthouse he had attractid opin mouths and many curius glansis and he repeeted now to the judge that he was fyne, thank you—for a hole month in fact, he went on in a Bold and Ringing Voyce, he had been feeling for The First Time in His life, exactlie like himself.

Judge Limbaugh noddid and wrot somthing in his jottur with a green mottld Pen. Pa reposishund his crutch under his left armpit. Trig jiggeld some coyns in his trousur pockit. Mr Hill the Prosecutur shuffld some papers, and behind us one of the baylifs drew closd the big oakin doors at the front of the cort. The chamber became imeediatlie darkur but this did not seem in any way to troubel James Elward, who was looking around in an intrestid way at the thinly peepeld cort—at the baylifs and the two lawyurs and at Judge Limbaugh sitting above us all behind his hie, slope-topd tabel on his speshul bilt-up block of wud. James Elward smoothd the skurt of his blue gown and tuckd a wysp of his fayre hair inside his gorze cap.

Perhaps he was biginning to wunder where the Andersons were, and why no discushun had yet begun involving Pigs and Corn. Or maybe he was letting his mynd wander a littel, and was thinking that after we were all done here this morning with the cort, he-ud take a walk into Jefferson with me and Ma and Dilly and Trig and Pa and Delphine, and generilly make a start upon his Futur.

Dilly, getting bord, leened her Hed against my hip. Delphine coughd, and there was a little clicking sound as Judge Limbaugh layd his green Pen down on top of his slopping tabel.

He steepild his long fingurs, and then he told us all in his lite suthern drawl, what we were about today, why we were here.

James Elwards mouth fell Open.

He gapd like a Fysh.

His eyes grew wyde and he lookd around at evryone as if the world had gone Mad and he cud not beleeve what he was heering. He began to laff in a kynd of slitelie crazie-sounding, disbeleeving way, but Judge Limbaugh told him to pype down and rispect the cort. Judge Limbaugh waved the prosecutur, Mr Hill, to his feet and Mr Hill—a squat, brissel-haired man in a stif collar and a gray tayle-cote—began with Ma, Ma the first persun to be called upon to describe the events leeding up to James Elwards sudden and unantissipatid transformashun—Ma the first one to aggree with Mr Hill and the Town of Jefferson in the Perlie-you of Larabee Countie and Under the Jurisdickshun of Judge Harold Warren Limbaugh that a witch had taken possesshun of Someone in our Familie, and that that Person was Dilly.

Dilly yes, Dilly, who-ud been movd by now away from the rest of us. One of the baylifs had takin her by the Hand and led her away to a small woodin box with a low hingd door on a platform by herself.

She was blinking and looking at evryone with amazemint and bewildermint and huge, fritind eyes. Like a littel Hors in a harf-opin stabel.

After Ma it was Pas turn, then Trigs, then mine, and last up was Delphine, and for a minit I wonderd if maybee Delphine wud-unt do as she-ud been told. Even tho I knew it didnt Matter what she sed, because evrything had alreddy been decidid and arrayngd, I was still curius to see if she-ud say it wasnt trew, or if she-ud at leest hesitate, or answer vayglie and reluctantlie, or say she cudnt be sure, but she didnt. She didnt say it wasnt trew. She didnt hesitate or say she cudnt be sure. She didnt answer vaiyglie or reluctantlie. She did evrything rite. She spok her lynes, and was as cleer and certin in her testimonie as me and Ma and Pa and Trig had been in ours. Maybee she was too fritind of Ma to do anything else, or maybe she just wantid to do whatever wud make Trig hapy. Anyway, like evryone else she discribd how Dilly was often to be seen clinging to James Elward with her arms tite like a vise around his neck, and how she had a speshul way of getting him close to her, and how James Elward never in his life before a month ago showd one single syne of ever wanting to do what he was doing now and how Dillys Witch had him completlie and totillie in her Power.

Judge Limbaugh noddid and made a note or two in his jottur, and now it was Mr Summertons turn to ask the questshins—Mr Summerton who Ma said last nite would be here to put a diffrint spin on things, because that was how it always has to be in a Cort of Law.

Dilly? Mr Summerton sed in a voyce that was not unkind, standing close to her in front of her woodin box and bending forward a littel in order to speek to Her.

He was a yungish man, Mr Summerton, with gingerie hair and a mylde plesant fayce. As soon as he opind his mouth, Trig's Hed bobbd out suddinlie from bihind Delphine and he shot Ma a worrid glans, as if he thort Mr Summerton, with his youth and his gingerie hair and his gentel, kindlie manner, might be about to derayle evrything. But Ma ignord him and lookd on wile Mr Summerton layd a payle Hand litely on the edge of the woodin box Dilly was in.

Softlie he askd Dilly, cud she feel any kind of Witch inside her?

Dillys teers were slyding down over her tawnie freckels and droping onto her pinafoor. Her botum lip was quivvering uncontrolablie.

No, she sed.

Mr Summerton noddid and turnd to James Elward, and asked him in the same kindlie way if he had actid these past four weeks according to his own desyres?

James Elward, who seemd carmer now, under Mr Summertons quiet and reesonabel probing, sed Yes.

Mr Summerton noddid incoraginglie, and James Elward addid that it was what he-ud always wantid. His hole life, he sed, for as long as he cud rimembur, he-ud wantid nothing els.

Mr Summerton noddid agen. He sed he was finishd. He sed he-ud nothing to add and no more questshins.

We all lookd up at Judge Limbaugh, who was making a large show of being supprisd by the brevitie of Mr Summertons contribushun, turning up both of his parms and leening forwid across his hye tabel. No witnissis to call, Mr Summerton? No evidens or testimonie to support what the childrin say?

No, sed Mr Summerton in his myld way. Regrettablie, he sed, with a small bow, he-ud not bean abel to obtayne any. Even tho he-ud lookd all over he cud not fynd one singel acunt from any other persun that supportid what they sed.

Judge Limbaugh leend back in his chare. He steepeld his fyngurs agen, and lookd from Dilly to James Elward and from James Elward back to Dilly agen—at James Elward in his shabie gown and cap, at

Dilly's Sparkling Curls and her tawnie freckels, her big cornflour eyes, her dirtie teer-streekd cheaks. He commendid the Teeg familie for its courige in coming here to testifie today. No mother, he sed gravelie, and no father, would wish to be standing here now in the shoos of Hanna and Michael Teeg.

Dilly and James Elward staard at him. They lookd afrayd agen, terrifyd. They gorpd at Ma and Pa and me and Trig and Delphine as if they thort maybee someone wud step forwud and tell the judge they-ud been missteakin and their testimonie was not trew, but nobodie did. Nobodie stepd forwud and nobodie sed they were missteakin. Ma coverd her fayce with her hands and Pa put an Arm around her sholdur, and Judge Limbaugh lookd hard at Dilly and in his soft suthern voyce he told the Witch Inside her to leeve, rite now, rite here in His Cortroom, and take her Wicked Spell with her and never come Back. Otherwyse he-ud have Dilly burnd.

Burr-und, he pronuncd it.

And if the Witch decidid to leave today, he continud, but Came Back at some later momint and stol her way inside Dilly agen, or if she made James Elward run Away—well he wud have Dilly burnd then also.

James Elward began to crie.

He stood with a Fold of his Blue Frock between the fingurs of One Hand. Oh dear Lord, murmurd Delphine in a tinie wissper. Dillys sobs came in short, rapid heeves.

Judge Limbaugh sed, I am wayting.

When it happind it was like the breef blooming of a payle blue flour—the fadid gown coming up over James Elwards hed: a billo of rysing Folds and then the hole thing collapsing around his feet in a wilt of duskie skye-colord Cloth, the four silvery hair-pins leeving his fingurs in a brite scatter of Sparkels disending to the floor, the whyte gorze cap floating down on top of them like a butterfly; Dilly, limp as a doll, takin up out of the woodin box and liftid into Pa's arms.

James Elward bowd his Hed. He had no Underware on, no Boys Long-jons, and he coverd himself now with his hands and closd his eyes the way littel childrin do when they are trying to hyde. From somwhere a blankit was producd and wrapd around his sholdurs. Mr Hill and Mr Summerton gatherd their papers and one of the baylifs opend wyde the big Oakin Doors at the front of the cort. Daylite pord in and Judge Limbaugh sed we may all go Home. Amen, sed Trig.

LYDIA DAVIS
Caramel Drizzle

"Caramel syrup or caramel drizzle?"

"Sorry?"

"Caramel syrup or caramel drizzle?"

This is an overheard conversation. I look up: it is a tall, slim woman with a ponytail, buying the drink at a Starbucks counter. She is wearing a dark blue uniform. We are in an airport. She is probably a flight attendant.

Long pause for deliberation. She has not encountered this choice before.

"I'll take the drizzle."

Now I see her from behind, over there, with her blond ponytail and sticking-out ears, drinking her caramel drizzle.

While she stood at the counter and deliberated, I was deciding that the drizzle was a smaller amount of caramel than the syrup, even though surely syrup must be involved in the drizzle.

Later, she walks away with another airline employee, the empty cup in her hand, the caramel drizzle inside her.

And then she turns out to be the attendant on my flight—her name is Shannon. So, her caramel drizzle will also be going to Chicago with us.

LYDIA DAVIS
Hands on the Wheel

I thought the booklet said hands at ten and two on the wheel. But maybe that's because I like to drive with my hands at ten and two. But the booklet actually says: hands at nine and three. Well, my husband usually drives with his hands at eleven and one, which makes me nervous. And sometimes—even worse—at seven and five. Or, when he's really relaxed, just at five.

LYDIA DAVIS

End of Phone Conversation with
Verizon Adjustment Person

I say: "I guess I'd better take your name…"
   She says: "It's Shelley…as in Byron, Keats, and Shelley."
   "Hah!…I'm glad you like them too!" I say.
   "Oh, yes," says Shelley.
   "I wish my name were Keats, but it's not…" I add.
   "I do too!" she responds. "Thank you for choosing Verizon Wireless."

LYDIA DAVIS
Second Drink

She knows the alcohol is kicking in when she thinks, wistfully, "Dear old Shakespeare!"

VIET DINH
Lucky Dragon

I.

The second dawn rose in the east, at nine in the morning. Hiroshi had never before seen such radiance. It rivaled the sun. He stood on deck with Yoshi, and the light crushed them beneath its purity. Hiroshi closed his eyes, but even so, the brightness pierced his head. The other crew members clamored to see this strange, unexpected light. But Hiroshi returned to the tasks of the day. He consulted Sanezumi about their current bearing. He examined the nautical charts, the curves and byways of the ocean unfolding beneath his forefinger. Last night, he dreamt of a large school of tuna, a flotilla so dense that the ocean became the blue-black from their scales. Their eyes flashed like diamonds in the waves. Each time the crew pulled in the nets, the smallest of the fish dwarfed him. They entered the hull without struggling, their flesh tender and firm, bellies thick and marbled with fat. When he woke, Hiroshi knew that it was an omen. Dreams were unreliable things, sinuous and slippery as eels, but morning had not yet come, and he felt the gentle listing of the boat with a single coordinate in mind: *east.*

But soon after the second dawn, Sanezumi pointed at a line of chop on the water's surface. The water recoiled, and before Hiroshi had time to react, it was upon them. The wall of air thrust over the boat, an avalanche of sky. Their clothes trembled as it passed. The men shouted, necks tense and strained, but nothing penetrated the ringing deep in their ears. Hiroshi's feet vibrated. His men gestured at the distant blaze blossoming from the horizon. Many had lived through the Tokyo firebombings—Masaru's left arm was gnarled with scars—but Hiroshi instead remembered the Philippines. His unit had gotten trapped in its position, and he hunkered down in a trench, face pressed against the mud escarpment. Mortars whizzed overhead; shrapnel fell like ice. The Americans were approaching. He felt their progress, a drumbeat in the earth. Only he and Yoshi and a handful of others were still alive. His comrades had sprung from the trench, guns raised in defiance, and were cut down before they had taken ten steps. Hiroshi should have been with them. In the creaking and moaning of the ship, he sometimes heard the voices of the fallen, calling to him from subterranean depths.

After an hour, the fire had cleared from the sky, but now came the rain of ash. It smelled of electricity. The men watched, mouths agape, awed by flakes the size of flower petals, warm to the touch. It clung where it landed, and when Hiroshi wiped it off, it disintegrated into a glittery sheen. It whispered underfoot. Yoshi flapped his arms, sending forth white plumes, as if he were dancing in a snowstorm. Some men held out plastic bags to catch it as it fell. Hiroshi looked to see from where it had come, but if the sky had once been clear and blue, it was now a peach smear. For a few minutes, the rain was a wonder, a miracle. But ash continued falling for the next three hours. It came down so heavily that the boat seemed mired in fog. The men dared not open their eyes. They left footprints where they walked. The ash gathered on the surface of the water, forming gray masses. The crew retreated inside, waiting for it to stop.

"It's inside me," said Yoshi. "It itches."

Hiroshi exhaled. Residue inside his lungs. He sneezed out pebbles. "You're imagining things," he said.

"I feel it in my chest," Yoshi continued. "Underneath my skin."

That night, the men were too nauseated to eat. In Sanezumi's quarters, Hiroshi rested a hand on his navigator's back. Sanezumi couldn't even keep water down; after each swallow, he retched, and the water rushed out of his mouth and dribbled onto the floor. *You'll be fine*, Hiroshi told him. But in the middle of the night, Sanezumi began vomiting blood.

II.

They spent two weeks at sea, slowly chugging back to Yaizu. Hiroshi radioed that they were returning home, that an unspecified illness had overtaken them, but they could not move any faster. The crew scratched without end. No one slept. They rolled on the ground, unable to ease their burning. They ate as little as they needed to to survive. Kaneda, the cook, served them rice watered down to a milky broth. Even so, nine days after the fall of ash, Sanezumi died. The crew debated whether to preserve his body or put him to rest. It wasn't auspicious to keep a corpse onboard, some argued. But others demanded respect: *If you had died, what would you have us do with your body?* Yoshi insisted on a sea burial. It was Yoshi's tatami mat in which Sanezumi had been rolled, and it was Yoshi's blanket that draped Sanezumi's body down in the cold hull. "He lived at sea and died at sea," Yoshi said. "It's only fitting that the sea take him back." The next morning, they gathered on deck, steadying themselves as the boat bucked and shuddered in the waves. They bowed their heads, and Hiroshi heaved Sanezumi's body over the side. For a short time, he trailed in their wake, but Ryūjin seized him, embraced him in foam, and took him to Ryūgū-jō.

The men feared that they would follow Sanezumi into death. But when Hiroshi saw the single character—*kori*—glowing on the horizon, he knew that they were saved. He steered toward the *kori* until he could see the wall of the ice house on which it was painted. The other members of the fishing co-op waited on the dock to gather and unload the catch. Miho was waiting to greet him. Sanezumi's widow was there as well, and when they delivered the news, her wails filled the sky, and the other women crowding around her in a rustle of silk and sympathy could not keep the sound from clutching her throat.

The next day, Hiroshi went to the Shizuoka prefecture doctor, who looked at Hiroshi's body and clucked his tongue inside his mouth like a wood-boring beetle. The doctor prodded his skin with a metal rod. Across Hiroshi's chest and legs, roseate patches had spread, the centers peeling off in thick flakes, and underneath, skin the shade of twilight. The doctor shook his head and suggested that he try Tokyo University Hospital. Their appointment was scheduled for a week hence. "In the meantime," he said, "try vigorous bathing."

Miho drew Hiroshi's bath and poured water on his body. He winced as it sluiced over him, washing away the ash and salt in his scalp. But when Yoshi went to the sentō to bathe, the boisterous chatter near the main tub stopped when he entered. The tub emptied of people when he stepped in.

"At least my skin has stopped itching," said Yoshi. A small comfort, at best.

At their appointment in Tokyo, he and Yoshi were greeted by a reporter from *Yomiuri Shimbun*. He bowed and introduced himself as

Nakamura. He held a slender notebook. Pens were clipped to his shirt pocket. "A student informed me of your condition," he said. "You were near the Rongelap Atoll on March 1, correct?"

"That is correct," Hiroshi said.

"Ah." Nakamura lowered his voice. "We believe that your illness may have been caused by an atomic bomb that the Americans detonated on the Bikini Atoll."

Were they still at war? Hadn't they already been thoroughly humiliated?

"A test," Nakamura continued. "A hundred times as powerful as what had been dropped on Hiroshima."

It made sense now: fallout, a black rain that sickened those with whom it came in contact. Yoshi's arms drooped at his sides, as if they were boneless. "If I may," Nakamura continued, "I would like to accompany you during your examination. Your struggle is the nation's struggle."

Hiroshi nodded, as if there were any other answer to give.

III.

Hiroshi no longer recognized his own face. This was not the fault of the photographer—he truly could not recognize himself, not even in a pool of water. His skin had dried and cracked and rehardened into an unfamiliar form. His cheeks were broken into grooves and crevices. The flesh had discolored to the color of algae on the side of a boat. The black-and-white picture could not capture this color, but he saw it on his hands, his legs. He rubbed his finger on the newspaper until his stippled image smeared, and he had merged into shadow.

He horrified Miho—he knew it. She washed her hands constantly. She handled his bowls and utensils as if they were made from lightning. She flinched from him, avoiding even accidental contact. He slept on the ground in front of the door, like a dog. The doctors had said that he wasn't contagious, but what did they know? They hadn't been able to arrest the spread of the illness. Even now it crept down his neck, onto his back. Specialists on radiation sickness from America had flown in. They waved Geiger counters over his body, and the wands crackled like sap-rich pine on fire. The poison was so endemic that it was inseparable from his being.

The government had towed the boat to Tokyo, quarantined where nobody could reach it. It still emitted high doses of deadly, invisible glow. Even so, as captain of the *Lucky Dragon*, Hiroshi's responsibilities now bore down on him more heavily than before. Hardly a day passed without a news agency coming to interview him, flashbulbs popping in his eyes, microphones recording every breath. Every picture promised a new deterioration—*Look what the Americans have done!* But not to him alone: his entire crew. They had all been similarly afflicted, but Hiroshi was the only one who had been photographed.

Nakamura showed him letters from around the world: China, Russia, South Africa, and so, so many from America itself. *You are in our prayers,* they said. *Our heart goes out to you.* Many included money, the stray bills here and there growing into a considerable sum. *Yomiuri Shimbun* had established a fund for the crew, but the money addressed to Hiroshi was his alone. He shared what he could, but this did not stem the tide of resentment. *You should have joined Sanezumi,* he imagined his crew saying, their hearts full of mutiny.

Yoshi remained steadfast: their bond was thicker than blood. They had seen things more horrible than an extra flap of skin growing between their fingers and toes; they had witnessed things more disturbing than the red sores appearing along throats like slashes.

During the escape attempt from the No. 12 Prisoner of War Camp in Cowra, Hiroshi watched his commanding officer, Sugiro, remove a fork from his boot. The tines had been compressed, like fingers inside a tight mitten, and scraped along the concrete floor until they had sharpened to a point. Amid the machine gun fire, the alarms and claxons, the screaming to run left, right, forward, Sugiro unbuttoned his shirt from the bottom, parting it as though he were opening a curtain. On his bare stomach, he pressed the point of the fork into his skin until it dimpled and bled. He dragged the fork down, then to the left, using both hands to keep it steady. Hiroshi bore witness to his bravery, his determination, even as Yoshi hissed at him to hurry, to run. The prisoners of war had taken a gun tower. Now was their chance.

Sugiro kept his face inexpressive, his mouth twitching only as the fork caught on something tough, gristly. But Sugiro cut through it and passed into someplace else, a place without walls, barbed wire, sandbags. What did he see when his eyes rolled heavenward? He knelt to one knee before collapsing, his pants cuffs and bootlaces blackened with blood. Only after he had fallen did his mouth relax into a smile, a blissful release.

Hiroshi tried to smile now, watching his reflection in his bathwater. Miho had added salt—the only thing that soothed his sores—and the undissolved crystals lay at the bottom of the basin like sand. His lips refused to form the shape his mind commanded. His face was no longer his own.

IV.

Hiroshi had not spoken to his father since the war had ended, and he had not expected Nakamura to contact him, but the past was beyond his power to change. Nakamura had wanted a quotation, and his father said this: "I have no son. He died during the war. My son would have died rather than allow himself to be captured."

Forgiveness would not come in this world, nor the next, but after Nakamura ran the quotation, Hiroshi's shame was exposed for all to see: he was a failed escapee, one of the ignoble. He had returned to Japan with his head hung low, chin attached to his chest. He walked, eyes locked upon the ground, as jeers fell upon him, as if from heaven itself: *Coward. Traitor.*

Then something further unexpected happened: someone wrote to defend him. Countless others had condemned him: FALSE HERO; A CELEBRATION OF COWARDICE; A SHAME UPON OUR NATION. But the letter supporting him—A VICTIM TWICE-OVER—filled Hiroshi with not so much hope as a fleeting, momentary peace.

"Look at this," Hiroshi said to Yoshi, handing him the newspaper.

Yoshi set it aside without reading. His lips were as thick and rubbery as caterpillars, his skin the color of new moss. "We were cursed even before we went to war," he said. "Our skin matches our souls."

"Nonsense," Hiroshi said—though he sometimes thought the same thing.

Yoshi spread his robe to reveal how the skin on his stomach had separated into scales, each as hard as a turtle's shell. "I wake up each night with my mat in shreds." Yoshi tapped his abdomen. "I bet it could deflect bullets," he said.

"It's still skin," said Hiroshi.

"If we were bulletproof," Yoshi continued, "think of what we could do."

This new Yoshi worried Hiroshi. Yoshi had always been solitary, but now the village people shook their *omamori* when he approached, and none would look him in the eye. None of his former shipmates, none of the workers at the fishing co-op. He remembered the old Yoshi, whose eyes widened each time they reeled in a catch, wondering aloud how much these fish would fetch at Tsukiji Market. The old Yoshi stroked the sides of the tuna, thanking them for providing him a roof over his head and a mat on which to sleep, and when the fish stopped struggling, he licked the brine off his fingers.

The new Yoshi's fingers fumbled with his robe, the rough claws and scales fraying the cotton. He ripped the sash, loosening it. He bared his chest, where the scales were as thick as a thumb and cupped the area above his heart. From his pocket, he produced his old service revolver.

"Shoot me," he said.

"Don't be foolish."

"It's a test. If the bullet bounces off, then this is a blessing. If I die, then you will have simply hurried me to my next life."

"I will not."

Yoshi dropped the gun to the floor. "I am unworthy of your friendship," he said, contrite. "Your loyalty."

Hiroshi placed a scaly hand on Yoshi's shoulder. He remembered their escape attempt from the POW Camp. Hiroshi covered the barbed wire with his blanket and flung himself over it. They clambered over the wall surrounding the prison, where Hiroshi found a dead Australian guard at his feet. He'd been bludgeoned, his forehead collapsed. The other prisoners spread out, and floodlights scoured the surroundings, picking out shadows fleeing into the nearby farmland. The prisoners had shed their maroon caps, which were scattered on the ground like pools of blood. The guard couldn't have been older than eighteen. Another boy pulled into war. Hiroshi felt at the guard's waist until he found his gun.

Yoshi ran ahead blindly, flailing his arms, deeper into the darkness. Searchlights arced above their heads. Yoshi's movements were panicked, like a small animal caught in a snare. Hiroshi caught a glimpse of Yoshi's arm, his neck. Yoshi stumbled and fell, and Hiroshi aimed the gun at where Yoshi scrabbled in the dirt. A quick and honorable death.

He could kill Yoshi and then kill himself, and when their bodies were returned to Japan, his father would wet his lips with water and cover the family shrine with long sails of white paper. His mother would hold the *juzu* in her hands, repeating a sutra for each bead, before offering incense to him, once, twice, three times. Yoshi would never even know that the bullet had come from him.

Hiroshi, Yoshi whispered, *where are you? Don't leave me alone.*

Close behind them, the prison guards called to each other. No matter where they ran, Hiroshi knew that their recapture was imminent. If they were captured with the dead guard's gun, they would be executed on the spot. Why was one death better than another? What was honorable about smashing in the skull of an Australian boy who was still too young, perhaps, to know pleasure? Had he died for his country so that they could honor their own? Hiroshi clasped both hands around the gun and flung it as far into the distance as he could.

I'm here, Hiroshi responded. *Keep going. I'm right behind you.*

V.

Masaru took a job in an American sideshow. THE HORRORS OF ATOMIC WAR. The poster showed him surrounded by oval cameos: midgets, bearded ladies, legless men. He made a good wage, the villagers said, and he sent back money to his wife, who moved up in the village's esteem. Miho overheard this at market, where she was overcharged for even rice, flour, and salt.

Nakamura had invited Hiroshi to appear on television, but he demurred and referred Nakamura to other crew members. They were men untouched by cowardice, and public opinion of them had swayed from disgust to pity, and now, to sympathy. It was possible that people thought differently of him too. Perhaps they were willing to forgive his conduct in the war. Strange: when he was a man, he had been a monster; now that he was a monster, he was once again a man.

Hiroshi's hair had fallen out, and the top of his head was hard and smooth as a helmet. Deep creases scalloped the length of his forehead, a permanent ridge of worry. Scales ringed his body like ruffles of armor.

Yoshi laughed at the news of Masaru. "You know," Yoshi said, "that his wife used to never touch his burned arm? Now she lives high off his deformity."

"We've had offers too," Hiroshi said. "They will fly us to America."

"Haven't the Americans done enough?" Yoshi said. He raised his arms, as if surrendering. "You know what people call us? They say we are *ningyo*. Mermaids! Already some of the villagers think that if they eat our flesh, they will live forever." He rapped his knuckles against the carapace on his chest. "Maybe they will break their teeth on me."

"*Ningyo* are omens," Hiroshi said. "To catch one is to invite misfortune."

"It's too late to throw us back," Yoshi said. He lifted a scale on his arm. The flesh underneath was gray and bumpy, like lizard skin. "What do you think I taste like? There's enough of me to feed the village for a week."

"You? You're as stringy as week-old beef. And if you taste the way you smell, no one would be able to stomach you."

"We could be a boon to this village," Yoshi said. "Remember the story of *Happyaku Bikuni*? One bite of me and everyone would have eternal life. They would hail us as heroes." Yoshi flexed his hands, the webbing as translucent as kelp. "Or maybe our flesh will poison the village folk, and they will know what our pain is like."

"Why do you say these things?" Hiroshi said. "Why can you not be at peace?"

"Look at us," Yoshi said. "Better to have died in Cowra all those years ago than to live like this today." He exhaled—a wheeze, a gasp. "You should have shot me," Yoshi said. "You should have pulled the trigger."

VI.

Yoshi hanged himself. Hiroshi found him—maybe Yoshi had meant for Hiroshi alone to serve as witness to his bravery, but the truth was that no one ever visited him. He had fastened one end of his obi to the pine beam bracing the ceiling and looped the other end beneath the scales on his neck, where the skin was still soft. A green forked tongue lolled out of his mouth, and his eyes were yellow, glassy, streaked with red.

Hiroshi did not cry out when he saw Yoshi's body dangling there, nor did he cry as he tried to cut his friend down. But his webbed hand could not hold a knife; his fingers were too stiff and clumsy. He slashed at the cloth with his talons until it frayed and snapped. Yoshi's body crashed onto the ground, and Hiroshi cradled his friend, scales scratching against scales. Hiroshi's eyelids had atrophied, but his nictitating membrane flicked ceaselessly to keep his eyes moist.

Soon, people gathered outside Yoshi's door, looking in, hiding their words behind their hands. The crowd grew as news spread, and it seemed as if the whole village were looking in. Hiroshi didn't move. Let them look. They had wished us dead—let them look at the result. He no longer had ears, but he heard them whispering, *If it's dead, we should have the body.* He heard Miho gasp. *How could you say that,* she said. *That's his friend. That's Yoshi.*

Monster's whore, they replied.

Enough. Hiroshi lifted Yoshi's body and walked outside. The villagers trailed him, holding aloft torches. Miho was among them. He smelled the detergent she used to purify herself. Here they were: a procession of monsters.

The villagers shouted, *Give us his body. Give him to us.*

If you want him, Hiroshi said, *come take him from me.* He gouged a nearby tree with his claws, and none of the villagers dared pass the patch of splinters he had made.

Hiroshi did not know if Yoshi's body would burn, as leathery and resilient as it was. And it would be impossible to bury his body in secret. What if it tainted the land where it lay? Hiroshi walked to the beach with Yoshi in his arms. Miho stopped at the sand. She placed his sandals at the start of the path back to the village, as she used to do when he went swimming. *The water is too cold for me,* she used to say. *But you go on.*

Hiroshi stood at the ocean's edge, the water sluicing onto his feet. He thought once again of Sugiro, the commander who had committed hara-kiri. Perhaps it had been the brave thing, the honorable thing. But Hiroshi had seen a new world blossom, a world born of light and fire, and this world no longer had a place for the proud, the defeated, the disgraced. The old world held onto its illusion of bravery, like the cowardly men up on the hill brandishing their torches, as if they had driven him toward the sea themselves. But all Hiroshi had to do was turn and open his mouth—his square teeth had fallen out weeks ago, replaced with triangular shards—and the men ran off like curs.

He no longer felt the cold. Even waist-deep in water, he felt no unease. Indeed, it seemed comforting. The tide pulled at his body, urging him forward. Yoshi's body was buoyant, and the sea lifted him out of Hiroshi's arms. But there could not be even the remote possibility of Yoshi floating back onto land. A *ningyo* washing up on shore was an omen of war, and they had both seen their fill of calamity. Hiroshi ventured further, deeper, until the light from the stars vanished.

He sensed the thrumming of fish around him: the mackerel low on the ocean floor, a squid curling its tentacles around an unlucky clam, and a school of tuna bustling about, mouths open and hungry. He breathed and exhaled through the slits in his neck. He propelled himself, undulating his torso, and as his eyes adjusted to the darkness, vast forests of seaweed unfurled before him. Fish darted out of his path. He released Yoshi's body. He swam forth, examining the endlessness of the new world, and Yoshi followed in the pattern Hiroshi cut through the water, almost as if he were himself swimming. *Yoshi,* Hiroshi wanted to cry out, *where are you? Don't leave me alone.* And Yoshi, now given to the ebb and flow of currents, called to him, *Keep going. I'm right behind you.*

EMILY FOX GORDON
Mr. Sears

Childhood is self-enclosed and timeless. In adolescence, a moment comes when we sense the future, if only vaguely and ecstatically. For me, that happened on a boarding school trip to Quebec. It was 1962 and I was fourteen. The circumstances of the excursion have gotten fuzzy in my memory, but I do know we traveled by school bus, and that a loudmouth named Warren played "Ape Call" (Nervous Norvus, 1956) over and over on one of those portable record players built into small suitcases. I recall that we stayed at the Château Frontenac, but I don't think that can be right. We probably only *saw* the Frontenac.

My three Buxton roommates and I were crowded into a small room. There was a lot of giggling, as you might expect, but also some serious talk late at night after the most powerful girl among us had fallen asleep and we no longer needed to fear her ridicule. On that trip I got a little more respect than usual from the others, probably because they could see that I was under the protection of the French teacher, who'd been counseling me informally over the past year. We'd been meeting once a week for half an hour after French class was dismissed. Our sessions consisted mostly of talk from me and receptive silence from Mr. Sears. The school was (and, fifty years later, continues to be) progressive, so I imagine that some committee assigned me to him for remediation of social backwardness and a tendency to skip out on classes. At the time, I thought he did it out of fondness, and he *was* fond of me, I still feel sure, though his affection was inflected by more detachment and amusement than I was yet able to understand. I remember nothing of the content of our talks, but I'll never forget how flattered I was by his grave attentiveness. Once, when some girls snickered at my new hat, he drew me aside and told me he found it fetching.

Mr. Sears was the second of four "male mother" figures to whom I became attached between the ages of twelve and twenty-two. He was lanky and tall and made me think of Aristide Bruant, Toulouse-Lautrec's stylish cabaret performer, the one with the red scarf flung around his neck. Mr. Sears had a similarly fine three-quarters profile, but he was elderly and far from raffish. Instead, he was slow-moving, deliberate, and dignified, a constant smoker with a much imitated habit of clearing his throat in the middle of a sentence.

I repaid his kindness to me by developing a devoted nonsexual crush on him, though that was challenged three times: first when I caught sight of his upper molars, again when it got back to me that he'd expressed skepticism about my claim that I was sick and should be excused from math class ("Emily is not delicate," the student representative who sat in on faculty meetings reported him to have said, "she is—cough cough— *robusta*"), and finally on the Quebec trip, when he spoke abruptly to me in the hotel breakfast room. I approached him at a far table where he was having a word with two sheepish-looking boys and asked him how to say "the bathroom" in French. I knew quite well that "salle de bain" was the textbook phrase, but worried that it sounded too formal for Quebec. I'd also forgotten that we were expected to speak French at all times. He turned to me and snapped, *"les toilettes,"* then went back to his questioning of the boys.

In those days, I was absurdly thin-skinned, but also resilient. By the time my roommates and I stole out of the hotel that evening at dusk, the sting of the hurt had abated, leaving me in the kind of dilated state that makes everything seem sad, but beautifully so. It was late fall, and chilly. The narrow waterfront streets were pocked with icy puddles reflecting the pink and blue sky. Behind and above us brooded the Chateau Frontenac. Ahead was the St. Lawrence River, partly obscured by what I remember as a dark flat border of squares and rectangles, like a strip of decoupage construction paper. Those shapes were docks and warehouses, of course, but I registered them as pure patterns. At fourteen I was as incurious about the world as I was receptive to its enchantments.

Our destination was a workingman's bar where some of the boys had boasted they'd been served the night before. To our surprise and delight, they served us too. The leader-girl ordered four beers in English and paid for them with three Canadian dollars (the Queen depicted on them was only thirty-six years old) and sure enough, four mugs were brought to our table and placed in front of us. Unprecedented! We sipped at the foam demurely, hardly daring to look at one another for fear we'd erupt in shrieks of laughter and the barmaid would bustle back across the room to confiscate our beers.

Meanwhile, a few of the men at the bar craned their necks to look in our direction. A little later, one of them shuffled over and dropped a coin in the juke box.

After an interval of amplified whirr and static crackle, the moment of annunciation came. The song was "Hey Baby" by Bruce Channel, just out that year. None of us recognized it—I wonder how it got to a jukebox in Quebec before we'd heard it on American radio—but it had us up and dancing before we knew what we were doing. Some songs come encoded with dancing instructions, and "Hey Baby" is one of them. Bounce on the balls of your feet, it told us. Rotate your shoulders, throw your elbows back.

It wasn't only that tripping, shuffling rockabilly beat that galvanized us; it was also the harmonica—Delbert McClinton's, Google informs me—and Bruce Channel's plangent wail. How happy that song made us! I think I was the happiest of all, because I understood that the girls had accepted me without reservation, if only for the duration of the dance.

Now that we were all in motion, a delegation from the bar made its way across the room to surround us. Most of their attention went to the leader-girl. She actually danced *for* those rough and dirty men, one hand on her hip, the other roguishly tipping an imaginary cap. The rest of us were thrilled at her daring, though we found ourselves moving in closer, as if to protect her.

It was while we were dancing that I felt the future. It came to me that our wild exuberance in this bar was the start of a great loosening-up and widening-out. Delbert McClinton's harmonica would sound all over the world, and everyone would be jolted by the joy of it. Everyone would dance, and in that Dionysian flood my dreads and embarrassments and my inability to solve for x would all be washed away. That never actually happened, of course, but something like it did. The sixties were on their way, and the fall of '62 was possibly the last moment before they arrived.

The Buxton campus sits on a hill overlooking Williamstown, Mass., where, confusingly enough, I happen to have been born, and had lived until 1960, when my family moved to the suburbs of Washington, DC. Why had my parents sent me back home to boarding school? Because I'd been doing badly in public school, and because I was hard to have around.

My roommates and I shared a big airy room on the second floor of the boxy, Italianate, large-windowed Main House. I can see the room, the Modigliani prints we'd haphazardly thumbtacked to the walls, the prickly gray-green vista of Williamstown trees we looked down on from our balcony. My distant memories, I've noticed, are slowly decaying. Spots of macular blankness have begun to erase what is focal in them, but even so, I can still bring to mind quite clearly the entire small Buxton campus. I can picture the Main House as seen from the road leading up the hill from Williamstown, reconstruct most of the rooms inside it, and follow the path that led from it past the concrete block lab and classroom building to the renovated barn that was the boys' dorm, and the theater next to it, where we mounted student productions. At one point, I landed a part as a member of the chorus in *Antigone*. We wore bed sheets dyed lavender, and when the spotlight was off us, we knelt in silhouette, arms raised in a hard-to-sustain suppliant position.

The Quebec trip was a developmental watershed for me. Before it, I'd tagged along with a few adventurous, rule-breaking boys. After it, I became a girl among girls. My roommates—the airy, affected one with the alcoholic father, the powerful one with the husky laugh who was far ahead of everyone in sexual knowledge, the heavy redheaded one who was truly my friend—drew me into their circle. Small things began to happen that gave me moments of piercing joy. Once, for example, when I was radiant with fever and confined to the infirmary, I found an envelope stuffed with notes from well-wishers on my breakfast tray. I knew that everyone who got sick got these packets— it was a school tradition—but somehow that only made me happier. One note in particular delighted me, sent by a girl so talented and popular I'd never have dared to speak to her. On a piece of buff-colored construction paper, she'd painted three watercolor bluebirds of graduated sizes, all perched on a Japanese-inspired tree branch. Under that, she'd written "A little birdy told me..." in italic cursive.

As my happiness grew, I continued to break rules—or "guidelines" as we were encouraged to call them at Buxton. In fact, I broke them at an increased rate. Periodically, the school's codirectors would call me in for a talk. Mrs. Sangster, the headmistress and founder, was a wealthy eccentric in her seventies, tall and benignly aristocratic, with an odd little flapper-style cap of yellow-white hair that sat on the very top of her head like a wig on an egg. Ben Fincke was a bumptious, bulbous-nosed man in his fifties.

Mrs. Sangster did the talking; Ben's part was to stay silent and look fed up. I was always terrified that she'd berate me for whatever I'd most recently done—smoking in the wrong place, sneaking off the grounds, smuggling in liquor—but she never scolded, never even mentioned my offense. She only required me to come into that dim room with its bamboo shades and heavy cigarette funk, every surface crowded with the wooden totems and lumpy ceramics she'd collected in her travels to Ghana and Liberia, where she "beat the bushes," as she put it, for teenagers to bring back to the school. She'd pat the seat cushion next to hers; I'd sit; she'd lay her big knobby freckled hand over mine, where it would remain for the duration of her spiel, which was always the same set of general remarks about how I must learn to see myself against the foil of other people. "So," she'd say when she was done, releasing my trapped hand, "we understand each other, no?"

Buxton was a good school, and at fourteen my intellect was awakening. Even as my behavior deteriorated, my class attendance improved. I showed up regularly for Ben Fincke's Civics course. He was a stimulating teacher, a prodder and a provocateur; from him I learned the joy of debate. Mr. Sears was a dull teacher, but I worked hard in French because I couldn't bear to let him down. The reading had gotten more interesting. We'd moved from the tales of Jacques and Marie in our textbook to Moliere and then on to the moderns—Ionesco, Sartre, Camus. Just to carry those books around was excitement enough.

As always, I failed math, but I did well in biology, and enjoyed dissection. With patient staring and some poking around with a gloved finger, I came to see that the organs in the wet and tangled belly of a cat were exactly where the schematic drawing in our text had shown them to be. Here was evidence of order in the world.

I was doing well, so why the misbehavior? Surely I was "acting out," but that was only part of it. The rest was the gleeful overflow of my new happiness. I knew that decanting gin into perfume bottles delighted my roommates (and was this not "seeing myself against the foil of others"?). I was the naughty baby of the group, which was a role, albeit a low-status one, and a role was just what I'd been longing for.

With the aid of our Cassell's French/English dictionaries, we in Mr. Sears' French II class made our way through Sartre's *Huis Clos* and Camus's *L'Étranger*. I don't recall that Mr. Sears ever explained existentialism to us—the class was conducted in French, and that would have been above our level of comprehension. Few of us had any idea what it meant, though we knew from reading about Meursault contemplating the guillotine that it was a hard doctrine, formed from sharp-angled concepts. It seemed to have no application to our soft young lives, but we found its intellectual glamor irresistible. For us, it was less an idea than a mood or an influence, somehow coextensive with English Ovals cigarettes and Miles Davis' *Sketches of Spain*.

Along came a person we took to be the embodiment of existentialism. This was Bruno Gaard, a man in his early thirties, I would guess now, who had been hired to teach the required intellectual history course and to help Mr. Sears with the boys by serving as a resident adviser in the dorm. He was handsome— "clean-favored, and imperially slim"—with a shining mop of dark hair, a habit of ducking his chin when he smiled, and an air of distinction that suggested he wouldn't be with us long. He wore a Burberry belted trench coat with a Black Watch plaid muffler, and soon many of the boys were wearing this costume too. ("I see it's raining on the continent," Ben Fincke remarked as they filed into breakfast.)

One of my roommates and I visited him in his rooms in the dorm. We were a pudgy, unprepossessing pair and had no business knocking on his door, but he seated us with some ceremony and served us tea, squares of dark chocolate, and sections of a peeled tangerine. We were charmed, and rushed back to the girls' dorm full of the news of our reception.

At some point during that spring semester, Bruno Gaard committed suicide. If I got the true account, and if the intervening fifty years haven't distorted what I remember of it, this is what happened: he and Tom Anton, one of the older boys, spent the evening in Gaard's rooms, discussing some book from the existential canon—I'm not sure which. According to one version of the story, the talk turned personal, and Bruno Gaard disclosed whatever the trouble was that had caused him to seek refuge at our school. According to another, it was a more abstract and general point of philosophical debate (the possibility of an *acte gratuit*?) that got him agitated. He threatened to swallow a bottle of pills, some kind of central nervous system depressant. Tom struggled with him and took the pills away, but eventually Bruno Gaard wrestled the bottle back. He stuffed its contents into his mouth, jumped out the bathroom window, and ran up into the Stone Hill woods behind the school. I don't remember whether his rooms were on the first or second floor.

Mr. Sears woke the boys and sent them out in pairs to search with flashlights. I wasn't there, but I can picture him, all composure abandoned, a wild-eyed, arm-flailing figure out of El Greco, careening from room to room, banging on doors and shouting, his sparse hair rucked up in back. He hadn't taken time to put on bathrobe and slippers; his gnarled old toes gripped the floorboards.

Bruno Gaard was found a little after dawn, unconscious but breathing, and taken to the hospital. It was one boy in particular who discovered him—I used to know his name. The girls were left to sleep through the night and only learned what had happened in the morning, when we were awakened early and ushered down to the faculty smoking room in our bathrobes. I remember the hush, the stifled nervous giggles, the baffled dread. When we had all assembled—boys, girls, faculty, staff— Ben Fincke told us the story, not sparing the dramatic suspense. He was several paragraphs in before he mentioned that Bruno Gaard had survived, thanks, he told us, to the heroism of the boy who'd found him, whom he asked to stand up, to accept our gratitude. We howled with relief, clapped, wept, fell into one another's arms. Then we filed out to the dining room, where the usual oatmeal and pancakes awaited us. The novelty of eating breakfast in our nightclothes set the rest of the morning on a festive tilt.

A week or so later, we were all called back to the smoking room and told that Bruno Gaard had developed pneumonia in the hospital and died.

During the days that followed, many of the girls wept. The boys were quiet and respectfully grim, though sometimes they forgot themselves and burst into horseplay in the halls. I'm sure that many of them have carried the Gaard suicide through their lives, especially Tom Anton, who tried to take the pills away, and the other boy who found him in the woods. As for me, I was a regular Meursault. I didn't feel much of anything except a certain resentment, as if Bruno Gaard had played a low trick on us by seeming to recover and then dying. I was also troubled and repelled by the picture of that elegant man desperately gobbling pills. The only lasting effect on me of that episode was that it cured me of my tendency to romanticize suicide.

That spring, I apparently had it in me to break one more rule. This time the offense involved drinking Chianti and ginger ale on the roof of the dormitory with my roommates. None of them were punished, but for me this was one infraction too many. I had crossed the line into incorrigibility, and my parents were notified that I would not be invited to return to Buxton in the fall. I wonder now whether my expulsion had anything to do with the Gaard episode; perhaps Ben and Mrs. Sangster had gone into house-cleaning mode. I'll never know.

I said a tearful goodbye to Mr. Sears, who, I'd come to understand, hadn't really been angry at all when he hissed *"les toilettes"* at me in Quebec, only tired and overwhelmed by his responsibilities as head chaperone. He hadn't been a party to the decision to expel me, and couldn't have prevented it. He was essential to the institution—who else could have kept the boys in line?—but held little power in the faculty smoking room. He seemed genuinely sad to see me go.

I was sent back to my parents in Washington, DC, and fell out of touch with him forever. Fifty years ago there was no social media, none of the endless keeping up that distorts and trivializes human connections these days. People often just disappeared from one another's lives, leaving to chance any hope of reunion. There's something to be said for that, because how can you think about someone who is never gone?

People wrote letters, certainly, but I was too disorganized to find paper and pen, and too soon absorbed by the excitements of my life in Washington. A year after I left Buxton, just as my vision in the Quebec bar obscurely foretold, the sixties had begun. More and more, I spent my afternoons not at the new progressive day school my parents had sent me to, but hanging out around the fountain at Dupont Circle. As if summoned by some inaudible signal, a growing population of young people—potheads, bongo drummers, runaways, dropouts, hooky-players like me—had started to gather there daily. By four o'clock the place was packed and buzzing. The native bums were forced out onto the grassy periphery where they wandered disconsolate and alone, like cows whose herd has been scattered by a thunderstorm.

I heard from my redheaded Buxton friend a couple of years after I'd been sent home. She called with some items of school gossip and the news that her father had died. She never mentioned Mr. Sears (whose first name, I'm just now recalling, was Henry). I take that to mean he was still alive at the time. Somehow I have the impression that he lived well into his eighties, in spite of his chronic throat-clearing. At any rate, he's surely been dead for many years.

I'm sixty-six now, close to the age Mr. Sears was when I knew him at Buxton, perhaps even a little older. I find it frustrating that I remember so little about our counseling sessions. My visual memory of him, though, is indelible, the clearest image I retain of anyone from my early life.

I see him, but I understand him differently now. When I picture him in repose, his head thrown back and his half-lowered eyelids veiling his gaze, I see a stoical weariness I couldn't have begun to understand then. He had a characteristic way of holding his mouth just barely open, lips slightly pursed, that looks to me now like an expression of chronic pain. Perhaps it was breathlessness, caused by his smoking.

Even at fourteen, I realized that his sense of humor was dark, and appreciated that about him—I could never have accepted an upbeat, positive-thinking counselor. Now I think it was even darker than I knew. If you'd lowered a spoon into his consciousness, it would have come back heaped with sediment, like the grounds at the bottom of a demitasse of espresso.

Once, during an ambulatory conference, he and I were walking down the long path that separated the girls' dorm from the renovated barn that housed the boys. I was complaining about something—I don't remember what—and exclaimed "Oh, Mr. Sears, I feel like kicking a dog!" Just then, Mr. Sears' own dog, a hyperactive toy collie named Muffin, came springing out of the tall grass and bounded across the path in front of us. "Well, Emily," said Mr. Sears in his considered way, "there goes one now." I've told this story many times, always inserting a "hem hem" between "Well" and "Emily," and I do remember that it happened that way, though it does seem incredible that I gave him such an easy setup. His comeback made me laugh, but it had the disconcerting effect of opening a door on his inner life, giving me a glimpse of a specifically adult kind of unhappiness, something quite beyond my understanding, though I'm sure it was only seconds before I reverted to my complaint.

Mr. Sears was the guarantor of my happiness—of everyone's, really. It wasn't just that I in particular enjoyed his favor, though that did make me feel pleasantly smug and secure. It was more general than that. His influence dispersed itself so widely that we felt him as a benevolent background hum, a steady emanation just below the level of consciousness. If it had stopped, the silence would have startled us.

We understood him to be different from the other faculty members, who all had their good points, but were also all treacherous or ridiculous in one way or another. Mrs. Sangster, for example, dropped names compulsively. She never let us forget that she was on first-name terms with U Thant, the Secretary-General of the UN—"As U always says," she'd always say. Ben charged the boys fifty cents apiece for private viewings of his third nipple. We gossiped about him and her and the others, but never about Mr. Sears. We imitated his hem-hems and told stories about him, but they were appreciative and respectful.

Nobody kept order the way he did. I can still feel the stir of his passage as he walked among the rows of desks in study hall. His tread was Jeeves-like, nearly silent, and he had a trick of sharply angling his downward gaze without turning his head. When he confiscated a note, he never read it, only folded it and stashed it in the inside pocket of his jacket. Then he moved on, leaving peace in his wake.

Nearly everyone I knew was eventually swept up in the sixties. Some were more deeply affected than I was, and had more to lose. For several years after I was thrown out of Buxton, I did a good imitation of running wild, but my fundamentally conservative instincts shielded me from some of the harm that came to others. I never did drugs in any serious way, though I dropped an obligatory hit of acid and smoked my quota of joints. I was too unripe to fall prey to sexual dangers during my high-school years (that happened later). Mostly I did a lot of sleeping in my clothes, and attended more therapy sessions than classes. The worst of it, for me, was that the education I'd embarked on at Buxton was suspended.

Several years later I took it up again in a most unconventional setting, a genteel mental hospital with an open-door policy. That's where I rode out the gales of the later sixties, and where I encountered the mother of all my male mothers, Leslie Farber. He was a psychoanalyst with literary leanings, a member of a small group of intellectuals in the profession whose practices were informed by existentialist thought. They were a little like cloistered monks, it seems to me, preserving an endangered tradition in an inhospitable age. If existentialism has survived at all, it's been as an influence on psychotherapy.

Farber's office was not only the scene of my therapy sessions, it was also my college. I read books, and we discussed them. The curriculum was heavy on the classics of poetry and fiction, but we covered a number of the iconic works of existentialism as well, and not only the French writers to whom I'd been introduced at Buxton. With appropriate warnings from Farber, I read some Nietzsche and—with his help—selections from Kierkegaard. He was dismayed by my ignorance, but took me seriously as a philosophical being. Roughly speaking, the upshot of our talk was that life's meaninglessness must be acknowledged, but that once it has been, meaning can be made. As Samuel Beckett put it with maximal economy in the last line of *The Unnameable*: "You must go on, I can't go on, I'll go on." (It was that last clause that Bruno Gaard forgot.)

To us at Buxton, existentialism had seemed like the coming thing, but in fact it was at the end of its career as an influence. There are many variants of the idea that existence precedes essence, but they can all be traced to two paradoxical roots: freedom and responsibility. In the sixties, the freedom root sent runners far and wide, but the responsibility root withered away. In that ecstatic and destructive time, existentialism became an antique doctrine, harsh and colorless, not exactly puritanical, but joyless and bodiless—a downer.

Through all the years since the early sixties, it's gone unrevived, probably because the ironization of everything has made it seem almost comically portentous and solemn. By now, it's nothing but an old trunk in the attic of history, rifled through by hipsters looking to borrow from the aesthetics of the bohemian late fifties—the thick-framed glasses, goatees, skinny ties, undersize corduroy jackets.

Existentialism was the first idea I ever entertained that had meaning for my life. But just as it faded away in the culture, it faded away for me. As I made my way into deep adulthood, it began to seem quite irrelevant to my situation. I wonder if it ever was a viable guide to life—to *all* of life, that is. It's not a philosophy for the meaty, middle-aged part of it, when you live in close and sometimes unchosen proximity with others, and can no longer afford to consider yourself an isolate. Like Sartre's waiter, you define yourself as an employee, a parent, a husband, a wife. Does anybody really buy the idea that this is bad faith?

Existentialism made sense to me when I was young. Now I ask myself: might it make sense to me again as I grow old? As my various roles drop away and I acknowledge, as I did years ago, the true isolation in which I live, might I find a new occasion for the construction of meaning?

In the twenty-five years since Leslie Farber died, I've thought and written a lot about him. He was a thorny character, and I've struggled to come to terms with him. By now I've finally metabolized his memory; he has slipped back into history. Mr. Sears was far less important an influence on my life, and for decades I gave him hardly a thought. But in the last five years or so, as reconstructing my past has become an urgent project, I've brought him back to mind.

What did I know about him? Only that during the school year, he and his wife lived in a small prefab house next to the boys' dorm. I remember the glassed-in bookshelves and the woodstove and Mr. Sears' rocking chair in front of it and the constantly yapping Muffin, and Mrs. Sears, who was one of those anxious women who stays girlish-looking, dashing back and forth with cups of tea. In the summer, they lived in a very old farmhouse with a summer kitchen—a family property, I believe—in a little town near the hairpin turn on the Mohawk trail. Another student and I visited there for an afternoon; both Mr. and Mrs. Sears seemed more relaxed than they ever had at school. Mr. Sears mentioned that before he came to the Berkshires, he'd lived for many years in New Orleans. I never even learned whether or not he had children, though it just now comes back to me that his nephew, a good-looking boy with a port-wine birthmark splashed across one eyelid, attended Buxton while I was there.

That's all I know, or remember. It's not nearly enough to answer my question about him, which is why he stayed with us at Buxton. At the time, I assumed it was because we needed him, which we did, but that's a primitively childish explanation. Why did he teach us the subjunctive and walk the aisles of our study halls? Why did he inspect the boys' rooms once a week and burden himself with my confidences? "*If anyone had told him ten years ago that he'd end his days as a doorkeeper in Marengo, he'd never have believed it."* That's from *The Stranger*, which I've just now finished rereading, this time *en Anglais*.

One thing I feel sure of now: his life had been a failed one. Not necessarily an economic failure: the old family house works against that hypothesis. Of the few clues my memory has left me, his remark about having lived in New Orleans strikes me as the most significant. It was, after all, the only thing he ever told me about himself. I can imagine him there, living a bohemian, Europeanized life. I see a young Henry Sears, not yet burdened by duty and irony, red scarf flung around his neck, bent over a manuscript at a café table. My guess is that he meant to be a writer, that he failed, and that after many years he came to Buxton in defeat.

This is speculation, of course. I can't know he was a failed writer. All I know is that he was a failure, at least in worldly terms. Just because of that, there was something admirable about his decision to take care of us at Buxton—a decision I like to think was conscious and deliberate, that he made and daily remade in the face of a lucid recognition of life's absurdity. In his own way, I think, he was a kind of existential hero. He would have snorted dismissively at this notion, of course, and like many warmly felt ideas, it probably wouldn't survive close examination. For one thing, it's possible I'm mistaking what was merely an automatic and unthinking WASP sense of obligation for the real thing.

Perhaps I shouldn't wish existential heroism on Mr. Sears. It couldn't be a happy condition. But he wasn't happy—was he?—though he made *us* happy. That was exactly the point. His self-abnegation and utter trustworthiness on the one hand, the despair that showed on his face and in his sense of humor on the other: those were the signs. I can see him now in the early morning mist, wearing his tweed cap and winter coat, moving his long bones up the path to the classroom building, beginning again the daily, Sisyphean, task of riding herd on us. He *was* a hero—or so I long to conclude—not so much a Knight of Faith as a Knight of Infinite Resignation.

Hollow Object

Beth tried to reach her daughter first thing on Sunday morning. When her daughter didn't answer the phone, a feeling of alarm arose and, like a weather balloon, kept sending Beth disquieting signals all day. Beth and Vanessa had a relationship marked by an almost occult sense of the other's welfare. Over the years, mother and daughter often called one another just to "check in" when they sensed something amiss, and often, in some related way, they were right. This constant fear for her daughter's wellbeing was uncomfortable for Beth. But the truth was, without it, she feared they would drift apart.

Sundays. The day of the week that bonded all peoples of the world in laziness. And this one was hot, rendering shade a currency. Beth knew that Vanessa hardly ever left her house on Sundays. She lived with the baby less than ten miles north of the college town in which she'd been raised, in a two-bedroom apartment in a sprawling old house at the edge of a Christmas tree farm. The big house was sectioned into separate apartments, but over time the residents of the house had developed a culture of their own. Now it seemed to Beth more like a commune. Residents wandered in and out of each other's apartments at all hours, and often cooked meals together. Most of them were single people, all of ambiguous early middle age. Beth often wondered why none were married, and what psychic wounds had led them there. But she was smart enough not to inquire. Vanessa was the only resident in the house with a child. The child—a boy named Chance—was eighteen months old.

Beth tried to reach Vanessa again at one o'clock, and then again at five. No answer. The little weather balloon soared across the backyard, the decking, the birdfeeder, sending its shadowy transmissions from an increasingly colder part of the mesosphere. Even as she sat with her iced tea and watched what looked like a rare waxwing visit the birdfeeder, her disquiet grew. That's what it felt like—a drop in barometric pressure, a hushing, an intimidation. With sudden sharpness, she remembered one of the many experiments she had conducted with the children, back in the years she'd had all three of them at home.

Her husband, Gene, had been packing for a business trip to the Midwest, when she noticed little Vanessa looking disappointed at the sight of her daddy packing again. So Beth improvised an experiment. She instructed each of the three children to give their father a hollow object. He would pack these objects in his suitcase and fly with them, so that the children could observe the effects of air pressure upon the objects. Vanessa, the eldest, gave her father an empty water bottle, the cap of which she instructed him to screw tightly at cruising altitude, for she already anticipated the outcome of the experiment. The middle child gave his father a can of aerosolized spray butter that he hoped would explode in the cargo hold. The littlest, not quite understanding the basic premise, gave her daddy an orange. While Gene was airborne, a cold front descended from Canada, and gale force winds swept the Plains. Beth didn't know any of this at the time—she wouldn't have heard the radio anyway over the sounds of three children squalling in the bathtub—but at that very moment her husband was riding through darkness in crash position, the plane plummeting.

The crisis lent the return of the children's pressurized objects more than a little profundity. The water bottle was warped, taking on strangely human proportions, tiny-wasted and crouched like a skeleton. The aerosol can had not exploded, but leaked a buttery juice onto the contents of Gene's suitcase. Only the orange was unchanged. The orange sat there on the bedspread like some kind of unholy icon. Something so simple as to mock curiosity. Sitting on the bed, one hand bandaged, Gene lit a cigarette and shook his head. The baby toddled to the bed and retrieved her orange.

Forget it, Beth thought: she would drive to Vanessa's. She would just drive on over there and check to make sure all was well. She drained her glass of iced tea, rinsed it, and took her car keys from the candy dish. The garage was connected to the condominium, and so she slipped into her Japanese hybrid and backed out into a sun that was brighter and hotter than she'd realized. The hybrid was designed to save energy at rest, and so the air conditioning clicked off at each stoplight. Every hundred yards or so, she and the hybrid baked to-gether in silence until the light changed. In this manner, she cued her way through a mile or so of strip malls and building lots until she reached the smooth stretch of rural emptiness before Vanessa's house. Fields of cinnamon-colored dirt gave way to rows of greens and lettuces, flowers, ornamental trees, and the occasional red fact of a tobacco barn.

At times like these, Beth desperately wished Vanessa had married the baby's father. She still did not understand why they had not married. A houseful of friends was good, but a child needed *two* parents. A man and a woman, a woman and a woman, a gnome and a banshee, it didn't matter. Two people who assumed guardianship for life. Two people, lest one be lost. But her daughter had been single for so long that she'd developed a rather inflexible idea of what a relationship should be. She called it a "contract of mutual acceptance." Vanessa insisted that any partner of hers would have to accept her just as she was, and never try to change her. She swore that she would also embrace her mate for all of his or her flaws. And yet when Vanessa got together with Morris—a sweet, lanky sustainable soybean farmer from Louisiana—the actual principles of the thing became confused. It seemed to Beth that the couple's relationship was a question of who was *less* attached to it, and who was best at being free within it, as if peace could be measured, like speed, in contest.

Well? How much to protest? Occasionally, Beth chafed against the sacrificing of her own principles, which she did in order to stay safely within the sphere of her children's lives. Objections she did not make. Warnings she did not offer. Silence appeared to be the price of the ticket. Years ago, her own mother had patrolled the peripheries of Beth's life like a border guard, offering all sorts of opinions and judgments. Never once did it occur to Beth that she might punish her mother for this disagreeable habit. But how the playing field had changed since then! For her daughter's generation, the sense of family had become somehow *probationary*. A family was a loose association of people who occasionally realigned themselves, like starlings on wire. You could pick a new family if you wanted to. You could move into a big house with a bunch of friends and that could be your family. She didn't like to think about it.

Beth pulled up to the apartment house and the car fell into its dutiful, thrifty silence. The house was a lintwhite, sprawling two-storied thing. Maybe it had a folksy beauty in its day, but it now possessed a greenish, rain-smeared roof, and one too many porches. The house appeared empty. No one stirred at the windows or sat on the large front porch or came around from the back garden.

The front door hung open, the storm door loosely shut and knocking in the breeze. No one had yet replaced it with a screen, even though it was July. Beth slipped inside, and crossed the foyer to the door of Vanessa's apartment.

"Vanessa," she called, knocking. "Vanessa honey? You there?"

A snap inside, a rustle, a tinkling, and once again Beth was in the presence of that snickering radiosonde, those short ominous transmissions, coming too fast to interpret. She blinked her eyes deliberately, as if to reset. A chain was loosened on the other side of the door.

The woman who opened the door was not Vanessa. This woman was as short as a child, an effect furthered by her paper-thin T-shirt and large, chunky glasses.

"Oh!" cried the little person, pushing up her bizarre spectacles. "Are you Vanessa's mom? Why haven't you returned my *calls*? Give me a heart attack. Calling you was like, the one thing Vanessa asked me to do."

Beth could not speak. The fact that she had been right to worry was still settling upon her with its exponential regrets. She opened her mouth and stared at the short person. Just then she heard the smacking of a child's bare feet, and the baby, her grandson, toddled around the corner and placed his face between Beth's thighs.

"Oh God," said the girl. "Look how *glad* Chance is to see you. That makes me feel even worse. Give me a heart attack why don't you."

Beth raised her head and fixed the person with a stare. "Where is Vanessa?"

"Vanessa's in the hospital."

"Oh no."

"Yes," said the girl. "Passed out. Out of nowhere. Curtains."

"*Curtains*?" cried Beth. "Is she alive?"

"Of course she's alive." The girl laughed clownishly, and then said, "Sorry. It's just been a little *tense* for me. Taking care of Chance all day. I don't know the first thing about kids! Well, I did my best."

Beth reached down and felt the hot weight of a wet diaper. Otherwise, the baby seemed well. His mouth was ringed with some kind of sauce, and he was wearing a striped T-shirt with the tag hanging out in front. He went to the couch and got his special hat, a gesture that seemed to communicate his readiness to leave.

"Which hospital?"

"She's down at Bay State. A bunch of folks from here went to go visit her and should be back any minute. That's where everybody is. She wanted you to bring Chance with you when you came. But I think she doesn't know, you know, how long she'll be in there. Tests, scans. It's a process. Am I explaining the situation clearly here? Sorry. It's just, when I couldn't reach you on the phone– " the girl held out a piece of paper to Beth, "I nearly had a heart attack."

"Is that a two?" Beth asked, squinting at the number. "My number doesn't have a two in it."

The girl slapped the paper to her head. It was the last Beth ever saw of her, and she never asked who she was, and Beth thought if she ever saw this girl-woman again she might strike her. She had Chance on her hip and was jogging with him across the gravel lot over to the car, his sandals hooked through her forefinger. She had nothing else for him, no clothes or snacks or diapers. There wasn't time. She strapped the child into the car seat, and only once he was safe and buckled did she kiss him wolfishly all over his face.

"Grandma's so glad you're safe!" she cried.

Tears bit her eyes all the way down Route 91. She kept glancing into the rearview mirror at the child, who was staring mutely out at the mountains. His special hat—a striped, old-fashioned red-and-blue cloth cap with a flaccid bill—was askew. Why had she wasted the day, taking no action? She *knew* that Vanessa was in distress. She had hesitated because she was afraid that Vanessa would scold her for worrying. For continuing to offer maternal oversight, as if she did not trust her daughter's ability to raise a child or to live alone without a man. No matter how much she praised Vanessa—her beauty or her strength or her knowledge—it never quite seemed summarily convincing. Vanessa was the smartest of her three children, hands down. A college grad, a gifted homeopath, she'd returned to work within weeks of childbirth, wearing Chase in a sling.

In the backseat of the car, her grandson laughed.

Beth wiped her eyes. "What's so funny, cutie pie?"

The child had curled his toe around the power lock and, with a satisfying clap, had locked his own door. He stretched his toes toward the lock again, and pressed it down. Again the child laughed at the sound of the lock clapping open. Beth smiled through acid tears: he had no idea his mother was in jeopardy.

"You're such a monkey," Beth said. "I bet you could unpeel an entire banana with your feet."

The child's gaze loosened. He seemed to be considering the image. That, or the word *banana* made him hungry. What he had eaten that day, Beth could only guess. The child smelled vaguely of bacon fat. Just ahead lay the low, clustered skyline of Springfield, suffused in the late evening air with a pink glow, almost pretty.

Chance wrapped to her leg, Beth checked the hospital room number and peered inside. The room had been darkened for the night, except for a fixture that diffused an intimate cone of medically blue fluorescence upon her daughter's bed. And there was Vanessa herself, dressed in a hospital gown, legs crossed, reading a magazine. Beth knocked.

"Hey!" Vanessa cried. "*There* you two are. Come here, my baby!"

The child ran to his mother, his cotton shorts bunched up accordion-style around each upper thigh. Vanessa squeezed the child in a rocking embrace. Then she pulled away and sniffed him.

"You smell like grease," Vanessa said. Then, to her mother, "He smells like he spent the day at a Mass Pike service area."

Beth sat in the chair that was pulled up to the bed. She took hold of her daughter's hand. "Vanessa, honey. Please, please, please tell me you're all right."

"OK," Vanessa said. "I'm all right."

Chance writhed away from his mother and slid off the bed. He toddled over to the vents by the window, out of which strong, scentless air was blowing.

"Are you getting good care?" Beth asked. "Who's the nurse on duty? Maybe I know her. I feel so horrible. A mother should *know* when her child is in danger. I am so sorry it took me so long. What's happening?"

Vanessa sighed hugely. "Oh, Mom," she said. She was still gazing at the child, who had lowered his face toward the air vent. "It's one of these hysterical medical freakouts. It's probably nothing, but until they're sure it's nothing, they'll give me just about every sort of test known to man. Scans. Smears. Finger sticks. I just had myself a lovely MRI. Do I look tanner? I couldn't lie still, so we had to keep starting over. I was laughing, it was absurd." Vanessa tossed her magazine onto the retractable tray, where it slid open glossily to a photo of two celebrities kissing on a beach, cupping one another's buttocks. Beth stared in amazement at the grayish crusts of an eaten sandwich on a tray, and beside that, the shiny Mylar mouth of an empty bag of potato chips.

"Look at all these," Vanessa pulled down her hospital gown, revealing several black telemetry leads. "Stickers. They've got to rule out the possibility of– "

"Of *coronary* disease?" cried Beth.

"Don't look so stricken, Ma. I tried to tell them. It's just the paint."

"The paint?"

"You know Marty, from next door? He's painting his apartment. I've been lightheaded all week. Those VOCs, in paint, I'm more worried about *those*. *You* know how sensitive I am to environmental poisons. Because, as you know, my lungs were totally compromised as a kid. By secondhand smoke."

Beth nodded and looked at Chance. The child had discovered the control to the mechanical bed and was lowering his mother's torso into a prone position.

"Your son and buttons," said Beth.

"And those things," continued Vanessa, on her back, "no one's even *studied* the connection between VOCs and heart failure. This morning—I couldn't even believe it—some aide was using ammonia to clean the toilet. And I was like, mix that with the bleach you've got there and you'll be dead from the fumes. In a *hospital*. Can you believe it?"

Beth shook her head slowly. She *couldn't* believe it. The child had climbed back up into his grandmother's lap and was now leaning heavily against her arm, mesmerized by the bouncing light on the monitor.

When Vanessa first arrived home after college, Beth liked nothing more than to hear her daughter recite what she had learned. After all, she had wanted to teach her children not so much information but a confidence in gathering it, an ability to say, I do not agree, or this does not square. A year or two after graduating from college with a degree in nutrition, when her book knowledge was confronted by the world's dark opposition—its astonishingly stubborn status quo—Vanessa's beliefs only became stronger, deeper, almost activist. The quaint old Food Pyramid was left to ruin. Vanessa came to believe that true health could only be achieved through a change in paradigm, a change in the entire way one lives and thinks. Soon thereafter, Vanessa had swept through her mother's house with a trash bag, and in went the cleaning products: All, Tide, Mr. Clean, Pledge, even her air fresheners, which apparently caused migraines and even depression. And her carpets were off-gassing toxins that were proven to cause neurological damage in lab mice. Even her tap water—potentially dangerous. Beth was rapt. There was an astonishing body of knowledge on these domestic toxins, and yet most Americans were ignorant of them, unaware that they had been forsaken by their government, which deigned to protect them.

Now Beth stared at her daughter, who had raised herself to a seated position and was looking back at her mother just as fixedly. Vanessa folded her large, tan arms across her chest. The white hospital gown flattered her, with its suggestive shoulder openings. She wasn't heavy; it was just that her body seemed to maintain an extra layer, a hyperdermis. She was a beauty, really, thought Beth, in the ample way of Diana of the Harvest. She would have looked good in a toga and rope sandals.

A nurse in pink scrubs tapped at the door.

"Hey, Edelma," said Vanessa to the nurse. "Come on in. This is my mom, Beth, and that in her lap is my little Chance."

The nurse stepped into the intimate light, the apples of her cheeks shining. Her hair was pulled back in a slick bun, and she wore large gold earrings that looked heavy as ingot.

"Pleased to meet you," said the nurse.

"I'm pleased to meet *you*," said Beth. "Thank God for you, watching over my daughter all day. And I didn't even know she was here. How are her vitals?"

"My mother," Vanessa warned the nurse, "is kind of an armchair expert on everything. Watch out. She'd win Homemaker Jeopardy."

"I'm a nurses' aide now," Beth clarified. "I went back to work several years ago, after a long hiatus."

"A long hiatus?" laughed Vanessa. "You mean your whole life?"

The nurse, ignoring them both, reported the vitals. All looked well. But the results of the MRI wouldn't be known before morning, when the neurologist came in. And visiting hours, unfortunately, were over.

Vanessa looked over at her mother, a touch of fear now visible in her eyes.

"If you could take Chance overnight, Ma, you know, I'd be grateful."

"Of course," said Beth, combing the child's hair with her fingers, its fine threads slipping knotlessly through her fingers. "Of *course* I will."

Sugar cookies out of a canister. Toothpaste with sparkles in it. *Handy Manny* movies. These were some of the indulgences she gave Chance when he came to stay in her condo. She even kept a spare set of pajamas there for him, ones that bore the lurid red face of Elmo. Chance was already fast asleep in his grandmother's bed. He had not been able to keep awake for story time. She watched him sleep for a while, then gathered him up and placed him reluctantly in a pack-n-play at the foot of her bed. Then she did what she used to do to her own kids at this age—she took advantage of the child's sleep with some heavy face petting and even some ardent smooching, the child's air-conditioned skin cool to her touch.

Her own mothering years were far away. She was not too proud to admit that she occasionally questioned the methods, the remedies. When she was a young mother, it was perfectly acceptable to give a teething infant a rag dipped in brandy, and all across the country, infants sank into a sweet, flushed sleep, and didn't feel pain. Back then, no one let pregnancy interfere with cocktail hour. Perhaps they were mistaken, but they were also *relaxed*. They knew that when labor came, someone would fit a mask across their mouths and noses, and soon after that they'd wake up with sutures and a baby. And it was all right, and nobody was traumatized. Because everybody agreed about it, so there was nobody left over to be a principled minority. Nobody to take offense. But many years later, when she had casually told Vanessa the story of her own Caesarian birth, the girl had actually begun to cry. She asked her mother, "How could you let them take away your most sacred function?" This had stunned Beth. Was *that* what it was? She had thought her most sacred function came later, when she was charged with proving the world safe against much evidence to the contrary, or later still, when she reached across the dining room table and the four of them—a mother and three fatherless children—bent their heads and gave thanks for the privilege of life.

It was the Cesarean story that inspired Vanessa to have a home birth. She announced this rather formally, Morris sitting beside her wearing cut-offs and a Ben & Jerry's T-shirt that brought out his magnificently blue eyes. Morris sat with one knee looped under his hands and was staring back at Beth in calm expectation. They looked so happy beside one another, Vanessa and Morris, Vanessa with her fertile ampleness and Morris with his bony, sun-kissed face. But in fact, the pair had already decided to separate by then. Neither of them seemed to have the slightest remorse about it. Morris couldn't leave his beans in Louisiana and Vanessa refused to raise her child in a Red State.

But the split, Beth knew, was also based on Morris' philosophical objection to parenthood. He had not wanted Vanessa to get pregnant. He felt she had done so in an underhanded fashion, and he was not going to compromise the belief he'd held his whole life—the belief that to raise a child was to hamstring him, to hamstring him in the Biblical sense, meaning, to cut the tendons in his legs until he bled to death. There was no way around it, said Morris, and no parent could be saintly enough to be an exception. It was just the hard, cold truth. What was? Well, he explained, first of all, the child is called into existence without his or her permission. This end-around sows guilt in the parent's heart. And everything thereafter, each parental action, every instruction, is distorted by guilt, and by the desperate attempt to prove life worthwhile. To prove life wonderful, and people good. Because if life *isn't* wonderful and people *aren't* good, a parent had committed a completely premeditated crime, about which he suppressed overwhelming contrary evidence in order to indulge his own smaller, greedy procreative urge. So instead of admitting this, every parent becomes a liar. He stuffs his child's gaping, impressionable childhood with propaganda. And the poor child, his identity is incoherent, composed of scraps—anecdotes, photographs, campfire songs. Every child is a stooge. Liars and stooges, said Morris. Who wants it?

When the child was older, Morris had calmly told them several times, he could come and meet his father. Only when the child was old enough to go toe-to-toe with his mighty shadow did Morris want to lay eyes on the child. And at that point, he would welcome his child with open arms. They would have long, honest talks, or fistfights, in which the child would beat his father with the ripped-off antenna of his car or a tire iron or whatever was in the kid's trunk of whatever car he drove at that point. But until then, well, Morris couldn't stomach the fraud.

The fraud, Beth had whispered, afraid to ask him to clarify. The fraud of *loving* somebody?

And so she began to miss him, Morris, even as he sat right there, asking her to assist in the home birth of a child he would promptly abandon. Beth watched him nod beside Vanessa, scratching his rangy, tan arms, attentive as any husband. Her heart went out to him. She realized that she loved him like a son. She loved him because he saw what was so wonderful and true and worthy in Vanessa. Just as she and Gene had seen what was so wonderful and true and worthy in Vanessa. Gene watched them, Beth was sure, long beyond the end. After he died, quite prematurely at 47, his presence had gone on, palpable for a long time. Perhaps from his vantage point, Gene had even watched Vanessa fold away the heirloom tablecloth, once all the mourners had left. Sixteen years old, a big girl in bangles, thanking the guests with a prim, storybook accent plagiarized from *Nancy Drew*. Morris loved *her*. That fat girl faking it at a funeral. Beth couldn't bear it, why all these people leave each other.

She dreamt about it all night long.

Empty fairgrounds. Recriminations. The way your body goes so limp when you're begging someone.

Chance woke up disoriented. He'd been frightened by his grandmother's face appearing over his travel crib. Then at breakfast, he had refused her offer of Cheerios.

"What," Beth snapped, taking back the bowl, "Not organic enough for you?"

She'd leaned with both hands against the sink, the baby's hurt silence behind her. She'd always had a hard time shaking off dreams. If you could remember them, then you could unpack them. Until then, they ruled you like slander.

The day was hotter even than the one before. She could see its heat out the kitchen window. There was a wilted quality to the trees. The smoggy heat would park itself in the valley and even the blazing sun would not diffuse it. The only hope was for wind. She was clearing the dishes when the phone rang. The sound made Beth's heart freeze.

"The neurologist just left," her daughter wept. "There's an aneurysm. He saw an aneurysm. In my brain. Unconnected to all this."

Beth could not move. It had come, the worst demon from her personal hell. She could not speak.

"I feel like nothing I know, nothing I've ever done *counts*. I have no effect. No control." Vanessa breathed a shaky sigh. "And they've put this horrible woman next to me, who coughed all night. I couldn't sleep. Do they really think a nylon curtain has soundproofing properties? Oh, Mama." She collapsed back onto this child's word, and Beth clutched her chest, so heartsick was she. "I'm *scared.*"

"Put him on the phone," Beth demanded. "Put the neurologist on the phone."

Vanessa laughed ruefully. "Just bring me Chance," she said. "I just want to see my kid."

They ran. Even the child sensed the urgency. When Beth could no longer carry him across the hospital parking lot, he got down and ran with his head down and his fists balled, trying to will himself faster. They'd arrived at rush hour, and Springfield had been surprisingly congested for a so-called disenfranchised city. It had taken them a half hour just to get from the highway to the hospital.

When they arrived at the room, Vanessa was sitting in her bed not reading, just staring at the wall. She wore her glasses, which someone else must have brought her, and her hair was heavy and unwashed. On the other side of the curtain, an emaciated woman about Beth's age smiled from beneath an oxygen mask.

Vanessa was slow to respond to them. She embraced Chance loosely. Her expression was one Beth had seen before—a wan, black look. Beth found herself acutely disappointed that she had missed that window of softness in which she might have been allowed to baby and console her daughter. Apparently, in the time since they last spoke, a second neurologist had examined Vanessa and ordered a new scan—an MRA. The new neurologist was equally concerned, but he was skeptical that the blood vessel in question was a true aneurysm, and assured her that the MRA would settle this small contest of prognoses. The two neurologists would talk to one another, Vanessa reported, sometime when Neptune was in retrograde.

"I am *never* coming to one of these *fucking* places again," Vanessa said. "This is *traumatizing.* I'm converting to Christian fucking Science. If I had been conscious, I would have refused to come here. I was taken here without my consent."

Beth nodded toward the curtain. "Watch your language, sweetheart."

"Watch my *language?*" Vanessa propped herself a little higher via use of her fists. "That lady over there is an idiot. She's on a respirator, but she keeps begging the nurse to wheel her out for a cigarette."

At the word *cigarette*, Beth tensed. She was relieved when, at that moment, the pretty nurse with big gold earrings walked into the room with a blood pressure cuff. She went to Vanessa's side and raised the sleeve of her gown. Vanessa was looking levelly at Chance.

"Hi Chance," she said, darkly.

"Hi," the child whispered.

"So," said Vanessa. "What did you do with Grandma this morning? Did she teach you how to read or something? Did she drag out that old abacus? Or the periodic table? Hey, do you know the difference between a metal and a semiconductor yet?" Vanessa stared down at the blood pressure cuff, as if she had only just realized it was there. She collapsed back against the bed and addressed the nurse, "When I was a kid, my mom here was always doing some homemade experiment with me and my little brother and sister. Making terrariums, raising newts, stuff like that. All sorts of edifying stuff."

"Well, that's good," the nurse said, not looking up.

"I remember one summer—a very hot summer like this one—Dad got me a baby pool that I loved. Do you remember this, Ma? I loved that baby pool. But Ma here decided that we were going to turn it into a pondscape. She filled it with rocks and waterweeds. And some actual *koi*. So much for my baby pool."

The woman on the other side of the curtain coughed. Vanessa was right—it was a deafening, body-shaking sort of cough, one with a prolonged, painful exhale.

Vanessa shook her head. "Sounds familiar, doesn't it, Mom?"

Beth looked down. Her neck flushed red. She could feel it.

"Yes," she said. Then, somehow embarrassed in front of the nurse, who was scribbling on Vanessa's chart at the foot of the bed, she explained, "We lost my husband when Vanessa was sixteen."

"Suicide," said Vanessa.

Beth blanched. "What? What did you say?"

Two little points of defiance sharpened in Vanessa's irises. "I just told Edelma that Dad was a suicide."

"I don't think you call it that," said Beth. "No. I don't think so."

"It's difficult to admit," Vanessa said, addressing the nurse at the foot of the bed. "Very difficult. A person wants her parents to love themselves. But my Dad smoked himself to death. Killed himself by lighting one Winston with the butt of another. The first one—*shftt-* "

she mimed thumbing a lighter, "before he even brushed his teeth in the morning. He cared about smoking more than anything. He lived for it. That whole house was filled with smoke. Ma here smoked too."

"You know I stopped after you were born. Im*me*diately."

"In any case, that house was always filled with smoke. All my childhood memories are seen through smoke. It was years before I made a connection between my asthma and Daddy's smoking. But I guess– " now she looked into her mother's eyes, "I guess sometimes you've got to be slapped by the thing standing right in front of you."

"That's true," said the nurse.

Chance's head popped out on the opposite side of the bed. He had climbed through the railings underneath it and emerged on the other side, inviting them to clap in surprise. His fine, straight hair—Morris' hair—poked out over either ear.

"Hi," he said to his mother.

Vanessa swatted the bill of his cloth cap. "Hi, you," she said.

She turned to Beth, her eyes overflowing with tears. "Take him home," she said. "Get him out of here."

Beth glanced down at the speedometer. She was going 80 without realizing it. It was a *hybrid*—she thought somehow that meant you couldn't speed in it. Breathe, Beth, she warned herself, taking her foot off the gas slowly. Why speed? There was nowhere to go. It was too hot for her and Chance to play outside. She did not possess a sprinkler, nor (the very words made her blush) a *baby pool*. They would be confined to the condo, to puzzles and books, things that seemed to disappoint the child. Chance. She loved him, she loved his face and his spirit, but his name always made her cringe. Whenever she said his name to others, women her age, she had to grit her teeth. It seemed so flip. She was still not ready to find the child's conception amusing. She'd loved him immediately, yes, but his name cast a shadow: Was Morris right? Had her daughter planned it all along, to become pregnant this way? The whole accident retained a chemical smell, the whiff of design.

They were nearly to their exit when Beth saw the sign for Mount Tom. She turned the car off the highway so sharply the wheels whined. The horn of a car she had cut off blared behind her as she slid down the exit ramp. Above her was the dark, verdant peak she had climbed many times with the kids, so many years ago.

She adjusted the rearview mirror. "Want to go up to tippy-top of the pretty mountain, Chance?"

The child paused. Then he said, "Nooooo."

"No?" Beth laughed shortly. "You don't want to go up and climb around on a pretty mountain, like an explorer?"

The child sifted through his vocabulary for that one. "No!" Then, sensing that he was going to be outmaneuvered, he whined, "*Mama. Mama.*"

"Fine," she said, putting the car into low gear. "I'll go have a look for myself. You can stay in the car and wait and be bored."

There weren't any real mountains around. But these hills were good enough. They formed a protective circle around the valley, and from their tops and lookouts a sense of breezy freedom and quiet could be achieved, hikers appearing and disappearing with their walking sticks, biplanes puttering across the bathwater sky. Along the crest of Mount Tom were a series of lookouts, and that's where she was headed. She needed a view. A place to take a deep breath and think.

"Your loss," she said to the child.

An arrow guided her off the main road and onto a kind of secondary access. She drove through a forest of cool-looking elm shade and then back into the bald, bright sun. A little farther on, there was a small, empty parking area, and just beyond that, a view of the valley.

"All right," she said, leaving the keys where they were, to keep the air conditioning running for Chance. "You sure you don't want to look at the pretty view?"

"No," said Chance, uncertainly.

She got out, and slammed the door. Hard. There: she was alone.

She walked the fifty feet not looking back. She was glad the child didn't want to come. Beyond a low stone retaining wall, the valley lay baking. Below the faint layer of smog, the foliage was verdant, the trees top-heavy as broccoli, obscuring all but the largest buildings—here a quarry, there a neighborhood. She stood trying to name the ponds and rivers, but soon found herself confused by the point of view. Everything appeared different than it did at eye level. *Relax, Beth*, she said to herself. Stop turning things into points of interest. She closed her eyes and breathed. But what was that dark bird that was beating there in her chest? She saw it soaring inside her, just as the hawks soared below her now, between where she stood and what they hunted in the valley.

Her skin crawled: the screech of a falcon. Over the years, the birds had become common in the valley, common enough that she could admit to disliking that agonized descending note.

That's when she noticed the silence. She turned around. Of course—the hybrid had shut off. Chance was gazing out the window with a damp face, his expression somewhat regretful. She laughed and walked back to the car. She was still getting used to the fucking thing. She couldn't really adjust to it. After decades of driving cars that ran continuously, it was impossible to adjust to one so different. She wished she could trade it in and go back to the old way. A regular old gas-guzzler like she and Gene used to drive. She had only bought the hybrid to impress Vanessa.

No matter. She had gotten to see the view and to take a deep breath and now was cheered by the little boy's face in the car window. He also seemed amused by something. His eyes, watching her approach across the heat, communicated a small joke. His leg outstretched, he fumbled at something with his toes. There! The sound of the locks clapping shut. The child smiled.

Beth tugged at his door handle. No: shut tight. She stepped aside and tried her own door. The handle flipped up and clapped back with mechanical violence. She walked briskly around the car and tried the doors on the other side. Then she came back around to face Chance in the back window.

"*You*," she said, slyly. "You silly monkey. You let Grandma back in."

His shoulders bounced. He was laughing, but she could barely hear it.

"Very funny," she said into the window. "If you're so smart, show me how you can do it again."

The boy paused. Then, bursting into laughter, he shook his head no.

She backed away from the car, trying to get some critical distance from it. The sun was blazing off the front windshield. She reapproached. The keys hung from the ignition. In the front seat, like some kind of shrunken head, her brown leather purse lay loosely shut, containing her wallet and her phone. She glanced toward the access road. The parking lot was dusty and still.

She looked again at her grandson. "All right, Chance. *Silly*. We're going to play a game. Can you hear me? We're going to play a fun game. We're going to play Chance Unlocks the Door with his Toesies. OK, sweetheart?" She could hear the uncertain tremor in her own voice. The boy looked at her closely, and with a fear close to nausea, she understood slidingly that she could *not* become upset. If she became upset, he would not follow her instructions. She covered her face with both hands, and then flapped them open. "Boo!" she cried.

The child laughed distantly.

"Funny Grandma," she said, wiping her brow. "Silly Grandma."

She straightened her shirt. "*OK*," she said. "Now Chance, where are your toesies? Show me."

A delay: the boy held up his foot.

"That's right! Now put your little toesies back on the lock you were just playing with. Wrap your little toes around that little tab—no, the handle." What the hell was it called? "The power lock. That little black thingy."

She tapped at it, indicating it through the glass.

"I saw you unlock it yesterday, Chance. Do you remember? How you were pulling it back and forth? Can you show me how you did that? Pull it. Can you unlock the door for Grandma now? Use your toes."

The temperature inside the car must have risen sharply; the child's aspect had changed. He placed a hand inside his mouth to the base of his fingers and was looking at her a little sadly. Through the glass, her voice must have sounded swallowed, different—did he doubt her identity?

"Chance," she said, unable to keep all severity out of her voice. "I don't want you to dilly-dally. I want to see you try it. *Right. Now.*"

Again, the child looked back at her. He scratched his neck with his free hand.

"I'm going to count to five, Chance. If you don't do it on the count of five–" she struggled to find a punishment that would rival death by suffocation, "–no popsicles when we get home. *No popsicles.* You hear me? One. Two. Three…"

Struck with inspiration, the child leaned forward, reaching for the lock with his hand. But he came up hard against the straps of his car seat, and looked at her imploringly.

"That's right!" she cried. "*That's* what we have to unlock. But with your *feet*. Use your toes. You can't reach it with your–"

Inside the car, her phone began ringing. Hearing the little jingle, the child became distracted and looked the other way, out toward the trees. She could see that his hair was already matted to his neck with sweat. She had lost his attention.

"No!" she cried, banging on the window. "No! Don't give up!"

She slapped the car window, but the child did not turn. She began to jog across the parking area toward the access road. On either side of the road, the heat made a nearly electric buzz. She stepped over a parking stop and onto the road. As she ran, the road kept turning slightly, just enough so that she could not see to the end of it. The mountain slope below her was thick with treetops, but nearer to the guardrail, the foliage thinned to saplings, and the scree and trash and bottle caps along the roadside made the sound of her footfalls loud and human. She stopped. She turned and looked back at the car, which reflected the sun blackly. She would not leave him, no matter what, there in the car alone. She ran all the way back and threw herself against the window.

"Please," she was crying. "*Please* try. Put your toes– on the– "

The boy's eyes were wide and dry. He gave her his own tears. He looked back at her with drowsy disdain, and this look said that no matter what happened after this, things wouldn't be the same between them, and they both knew it. He turned forward, as if he were waiting for someone else altogether.

"Damn you!" she cried. "It's easy! It's simple! Put your toes on the lock and pull up!" She clawed at her hair. "Just *do* it! *Try* it, god damn you! God *damn* you!"

The pickup pulled in before she even heard it approaching. A low, grumbling sound of a vehicle kept together with spit and staples. Beth, who had slid to her knees beside the car, looked up. A man about her age was peering down at her through the open window. His concerned expression brought her back to earth, providing her with a reflection of her snotted face, her sweat-stained blouse and dusty shoes.

"Can you help me?" she asked him.

He smiled then, this stranger, rolling his eyes at the locked car and the child in the back, who was hot and sweaty but still alive apparently, although Beth felt too weak and too disbelieving to check. She stared at the man. He was shaking his head as if he knew it all already, as if he'd done this already, or as if he knew what it meant to be her, to be a grandmother with a grandmother's rights, to live alone in a condominium with your collection of field guides, to keep getting slammed for your stupid mistakes, in perpetuity, and to have to keep your dumb love in trust, to keep your love warm and ready until, all other options exhausted, your love might prove finally acceptable to the beloved. She was sorry. She was sorry. But when would this release her? The man was rummaging in this backseat, looking for a hanger (you wouldn't *believe* how often it came in handy), or hammer (if we have to break the window), or—and this she dreamed darkly—a shotgun to kill her with. Any one of those would do. She could not bear it anymore. She did not care how it ended.

She watched the man work. He kept talking calmly over the sound of his engine, trying to reassure her with his own lack of worry. He would help her, it would be all right. She did not count the seconds. The heat had gotten to her too, and through it, she made odd associations. For he reminded her of someone, this stranger did. That was it—Morris, an older version of Morris. The same stiff hair, gray now. The same blue eyes that seemed to know so much.

After the home birth, after the baby had been born and placed in Vanessa's lap, Morris had smiled, wiped the tears from his eyes, and gone to shower. It had been such a joyful thing, the home birth. Vanessa had been right to insist on it. There was something sacred about it, the honor of watching Vanessa and the midwife toil for hours in that old rambling house and taking walks in the garden to squat under the sun, the other residents bringing them lemonade, chipped ice, sliced cold tomatoes, as they all waited in a loving hush for love to come. Beth had never felt closer to any human beings in her life. How *long* it had gone on, no one demanding an end to it. And so, after the baby was born and cleaned and swaddled, and all the residents had come through to give their blessings, though it should not have been a surprise, she was devastated by the sight of Morris' bags by the door.

Well, he had said. *Time to get going.*

Morris stepped into the room and watched Vanessa and the nursing infant. Then Vanessa raised her head, and the pair exchanged a look Beth had never seen before. Her daughter's eyes mellowed, as if through some holy generosity she was freeing him from the burden of being consequential.

On his way out, Morris had passed Beth and put one hand on her shoulder in farewell. But she couldn't do it. She couldn't let him go. She had grabbed his arm and pulled him into an embrace so strong it was clear he was meant to reconsider. To stay, if her own heartache meant anything to him. If he cared about her welfare, as well as his own child's. Embracing him, she shut her eyes tightly and pulled his head down close to hers. She could taste his wet hair in her mouth.

We love you, she whispered into Morris' ear. *Don't go.*

I've got to, he replied.

But I don't understand, she pled. *That's your child.*

Let him go, Mom, came her daughter's low voice from across the room.

Morris stood there stiffly, with Beth's arms locked around him. She could not let him go, but at the same time, she understood that her not letting him go was proving him right. She could not let him go, but that had little to do with him. When she held on past the point of embarrassment, a groan came from Morris' throat and he surprised her by pressing her head close to his mouth, so that his breath was humid in her ear.

Sister, he said. *You don't understand it because you're too far into it. Quit trying to understand it. If you understood it, you'd explode.*

GEORGI GOSPODINOV
Sonning a Father

Translated by Angela Rodel

The Runt had no luck with fathers at all. On the whole, nobody here had any luck with parents, but most of them were always crying for their mothers. The orphanage that they came from was itself called "Mother and Child" for some unknown reason. First, there were no mothers there. And second, only girls want mothers. Men need fathers. But there was no "Father and Child" orphanage. Nobody could say why. All the fathers have gone to the dogs, his friend Ceca the cook would laugh. He was seven already, one of the elders in the orphanage. There wasn't a single man in the whole orphanage besides the doorman, Mihal the Gimp. He had only one arm, but he could thrash you with it as if for two. He wore an old peaked cap, his empty sleeve was tucked into the belt of his uniform jacket, he almost never spoke, he just doled out beatings. If he wanted to say "hi," he would simply smack you upside the head. That was his language. That's all he's ever known, the matrons would say in his defense. Everyone steered clear of him. He wasn't father material at all. A father doesn't beat you every time he catches sight of you. Yet the Runt really wanted a father. He was already at an advanced age for adoption, a geezer (that's what Ceca called him); besides, in these tough times who would take on a foster child?

And then one day, the Runt saw him, just like that, as he was staring out the window of the room. The big chestnut tree at the end of the yard. He snuck out that very afternoon after class and went over to him. He circled the tree, touching the bark, looking him over from all sides, sizing him up. Yes, he would make a good father; he had everything it took, he was hulking, with big branches. A lot bigger than Mihal the Gimp. And he would never beat him. I'll son you as my father, he told the tree. He had come up with this phrase: sonning a father. Since men can father sons, that must mean boys can son fathers. The chestnut silently consented. So the Runt started sonning his new father. He would go out to see him every afternoon. He would tell him about

Seko and Teko, twins who were the class hell-raisers; about Nayden the Fatty, who had a grandfather and would completely show off when his grandfather came to take him out on Sunday afternoons; about Ceca the cook; about the cellar full of coal, where they would sometimes punish him...

One day, the twins followed him and heard him talking to the tree. They jumped out from behind him and started making fun of him. They were beanpoles, each a whole head taller than he was. Man, I really gotta pee, one of them said, and they pulled down their pants and started pissing on his father. This was too much. The Runt ran at them and started pounding them with his puny fists. At first, they couldn't believe it, then they caught him, twisted his arms behind his back and started wailing away at him. The Runt didn't give up, he tried to kick and bite, he didn't want his father to be the least bit ashamed of him. Luckily, at that moment one of the matrons turned up and rescued him.

But the worst was yet to come. Toward the end of the year, in late autumn, the chestnut started drooping, its leaves turned rusty, covered with brown spots, it got sick, and started drying up. Word started going around that it wasn't worth a darn anyway, that it was just taking up space that could be used for a nice coal shed. And so one day, Grandpa Stamo from the village arrived with his chainsaw.

They were all in class when they heard the sound of the machine. The Runt immediately realized what was happening, jumped up from his desk, ran out of the room, and bolted toward the tree. He passed the stunned Mihal like a streak of light and reached his father before the woodcutter could sink his blade into him. He grabbed the lowest branch and pulled himself up, then climbed over to another and in a few seconds was at the top of the tree. He was standing among the branches like a terrified little beast, shaking and looking at the old man, who had turned off his chainsaw. I won't let you take him, the Runt yelled, I'll have you know! He sensed that as long as he was up here with him, his father was safe.

The matrons had started gathering down below, Mihal was pacing around like a wolf and tossing his head, but there was no way he could climb up with one arm. The principal arrived as well. Get down from there immediately, she commanded, and the Runt could see the big iron ring on her finger. They were all afraid of it. She didn't beat you with a switch as the others did, she didn't pummel you with her fists, like Mihal, she would just rap you on the head with her heavy ring. I'm not coming down, the Runt said quietly. The whole business ground to a halt. It wouldn't do to call the fire department all the way from town because of one kid. Mihal was growling ever more furiously and the Runt knew what he was in for if he came down. Then Ceca the cook, his friend, said something to the principal and called out to him. If you come down now, you'll get off scot-free and you won't get a beating. Here, the principal herself will tell you so. The principal nodded. The Runt was silent for a bit, then shook his head: no. He wouldn't betray his father so easily. I'll come down, he said, if you promise not to slaughter him. Two of the matrons had to stifle their laughter. And if you make Grandpa Stamo go home with his chainsaw. I'm going to tan your hide, the principal hollered, but Ceca said something to her. Fine, the principal said, Grandpa Stamo will go home, and you'll come down.

The old man hoisted the chainsaw onto his shoulder and set off ever so slowly toward the village. The Runt hesitated for a few more minutes. Were they telling the truth? Don't worry, he told the tree, stroking the branch he was sitting on, and slowly started climbing down. He had to pee really badly in any case. But as soon as his foot touched the ground, he felt Mihal's iron grip. They dragged him toward the coal cellar, where the "torture chamber," as they called it, was. Ceca the cook was following them, telling Mihal "no beatings now, you heard the principal." And sure enough, he miraculously got off without a beating, they just locked him up downstairs.

From the window he could see the yard and after ten minutes or so, he was stunned to hear the noise of the chainsaw. They had lied to him…He plugged his ears, squeezed his eyes shut, and sank down into a corner; he didn't want to hear and see them slaughtering his only father.

The Runt found his second father the following year. He was now eight. They delivered a bust of Stalin to the orphanage. New, handsome, made of plaster, an exact copy of the real thing. At the unveiling of the bust, the principal called Stalin the "father of the peoples." And so the word *father* burrowed into his head. Since he is the father of whole peoples, that means that at least a small, ant-size slice of Stalin was his father too. He kept finding excuses to hang around the bust; if there was no one nearby, he even got up the courage to touch it. This time no one dared make fun of him, everyone was afraid of this father of his.

To ring in the new year of 1956, the local factory gave them toys— dolls for the girls and rifles for the boys. Fine, so they were assembly-line rejects, the dolls' heads were inordinately swelled, and the rifles' barrels were crooked, but who's looking that closely? And in the evening after everyone had gone to bed and even Mihal had fallen asleep, the Runt got up and went over to Papa Stalin to show him the rifle. He knew his father was an expert in weapons, he was a generalissimus, the highest-ranking one in the world. And his father looked over his rifle with a knowing eye, squinting slightly. It was his best New Year's ever, for the first time he had gotten a present and spent the whole evening with a father.

Four months later, as he was running to say "good morning" to his father as usual, he stopped dead in his tracks in front of the teachers' lounge. His father was gone. The pedestal that the bust had been resting upon only a day earlier was empty. He didn't have anyone else to ask besides the cook. Her explanation confused him completely. First, it turned out that his father had died three years earlier, but nobody had mentioned that at the orphanage. The teacher had claimed that he was alive and taking care of us and…And second, we suddenly found out that he wasn't quite what we had thought he was. But she refused to tell him anything more.

That whole spring, the Runt could not figure out why they had gotten rid of the bust of his father, the *generalissimus*—he had just learned to roll the word off his tongue—and whether he really could have been such a bad father of the peoples. For him, he had been a perfectly fine father.

Summer passed, autumn came, they moved him to an orphanage for older children, but the Runt was always on the lookout for a suitable father. He wanted to give it one more try. On Sundays, when the place was more deserted, he would slip through a hole in the fence and wander around. The orphanage was isolated at the upper end of the small town, far from the last houses; most often there wasn't a living soul in sight. Then one day, a dog appeared out of the nothingness. He surely must have been dumped there by someone. The Runt went over to him, but he didn't budge, he wasn't afraid. He hugged the dog. For the first time, he was hugging something that was warm and alive. Papa Chest- nut had been hard to the touch, Papa Stalin had been cold, but his new father was warm, with a wet nose and soft fur. He tied a few tree branches together with wire and made him a little hut in the bushes alongside the road.

He started running away every other day or so; he would slip through the fence, carrying a crust of dried bread from the kitchen for his father, and the two of them would sit and talk. He told him about how one of the teachers was taken straight from the classroom one day and, hustled into a jeep, and how she never came back again. About how once they had told him to go downstairs because his mother and father were waiting for him, and how even though he knew those parents didn't exist he still flew down the stairs barefoot, but it turned out to be a mistake, they were there for the other Dimcho. He finally told him about pretty Lena, with the sad eyes, who had been giving him looks, but he didn't have a clue what to do. His father simply listened and looked him straight in the eye; no one had ever listened to him for that long before.

In the winter, the Runt pinched an ancient quilted jacket from the basement and brought it there for his father to sleep on. It was also cold at the orphanage that year, there wasn't enough coal, and he would tell his father how they had started sleeping two to a bed to keep warm.

The Runt lived long and happily with his third father for four and a half years. One spring day, when everything was flowing and chirping, the Runt didn't find his father in the hut. He whistled and looked around, wondering how to call him, he hadn't given him a name. Daaad…He listened, but didn't hear anything. Daaaad!…he called more loudly. He saw a truck stopped at the end of the road, at the turn-off to the city. He ran over as fast as he could, as he got closer he saw men with rifles standing around and it was all clear to him. Two of them were just tossing a dog's corpse into the truck. What's wrong, boy, seen any other stray mutts hanging around here? He turned around so they wouldn't see him cry, and headed back the way he'd come. He was already thirteen, he had grown quite a bit, his nickname hung on him like a tattered shirt. He burst out crying only when he reached the hut. He who hadn't cried when they locked him up with the coal or when Mihal the Gimp had thrashed him. Who were these people, not worth a darn as fathers, but who always killed a father as soon as they spotted one?

That very day, the Runt decided not to son any more fathers. A week later he found two abandoned, practically blind kittens in the basement and adopted them. Now he was a father.

Here Is Where

Jim Carlyle drove down Glenmore's main street looking for a parking spot in a manner that suggested he'd never burned out a clutch in sixty years of driving and wasn't about to start now. He found a place and swung the Utility's wheel so that he rolled in perfectly against the kerb. Nothing wrong with his reflexes. He just drove at a speed that let him count steers in a paddock or check where a branch might have dropped over the fence. Always had. Never put a car into a ditch, never lost control on some back road, not in sixty years. Sixty-three, more like. He didn't even have to wear a seat belt now—that was the new thing the doctors had worked out for him when he'd had the stent put in, after that little scare he'd had. Not a stroke exactly. They'd explained it to him, drawn a diagram. A small bleed, so that his brain had taken a while to repatch its circuits and relearn the old connections. Wearing a seat belt might have put pressure on his carotid artery, so he was exempt. Had a sticker on his license and all. He'd driven around for a while half hoping one of these young coppers in town would pull him over and try to book him so he could bring out that sticker, but to his secret disappointment, so far nobody had.

He paused a few moments after turning off the ignition, just watching a mother herding her kids into the library. He'd been at the opening of that library. Good few years back now. He still liked the architecture. That had been a good era; the biscuit-coloured bricks with the square banks of windows, things crisp and clean and full of no-nonsense right angles, which suggested that tasks were being sorted and accomplished inside. Jim had been on council when they approved the new chamber of commerce too and still had a book at home showcasing towns of the district with a black-and-white photo of that chamber taken the year it was finished. The chairs all squared up round the table. What had that table been? Danish wood, maybe. Or teak, back when Malaysia was still Malaya. The caption. Give him a second. *"State-of-the-art style in Council Chambers just completed in Glenmore"* and by God, he could have put his hand on that book right now if you asked him; he could see it on the hallway shelf exactly where it was, stacked on top of all the

LP records the kids had left behind, all the hardcovers tidily together, and as he sat there he could smell that hallway, the faint dust in the hall runner and Margie's little bowl of rose potpourri scenting the air.

Jim had one of the faint foundering moments he sometimes had, a burring, churning minute where something in the calibrations seemed to lift and judder. A short blank hole he needed to rouse himself from, but easy to ignore, apart from bracing for the jagged little spurt of nausea that followed. Half a block back to the hardware. Yes. He'd have a poke through the bolts and find one that would do the job for the gate at the stockyards, a job that would need predrilling first, so he might get Jack onto that because something about that new cordless drill, the grip and pressure you needed on it, just didn't suit him anymore, he couldn't get a firm enough grasp. Some bolts and maybe a length of chain, if they had something that wasn't from China.

He eased himself out of the cabin, countering the nausea with a calculation of how many years it had been since the day he'd walked into the hardware store to find Vince had started there. 1964, so fifty years. Vincenzo Geroni. His English hadn't been good and hadn't he been made to feel it, standing there fresh off the boat, 1964 and the country full of New Australian migrants but not too many of them beached in Glenmore and poor Vince learning that the hard way, having left behind God knows what back in Italy to sell paint and brooms and nails to farmers who took their time pretending not to understand him. Jim had stood there, hurting for him in his white shirt and oiled hair, watching Frank LaSalle raising his voice like the man was an idiot—Frank saying, "Mate, if you don't know what a shifter is maybe you'd better get the manager, comprendee?", enjoying himself over it, no motive except meanness.

Jim had waited his turn, then fished what he'd brought with him out of his pocket—the rubber seal Margie had given him off her coffee pot that had started to perish. She'd got a taste for that boiled coffee ever since some friend had given her the Italian stovetop coffee maker for a wedding present, bought from some continental shop in Melbourne. The rocket, she called it. Jim remembered taking an apologetic breath, ready to explain. But Vince had glanced at it and his whole face flooded with relief. He'd taken the rubber ring and said: "Yes, yes! Vittoria eight cup, yes?" Just knowing straightaway. Then out the back and up a ladder, hand straight to the box on the top shelf, and bringing out a new one, and Jim introducing himself. And Vince saying to him—in that mangled English that just hurt your heart to listen to, it came at such a cost with such shut-up feeling behind it—Vince stooping down impulsively to touch the polished timber floor and saying he could tell Australia was a rich country, because just look at the wood they used for their floorboards here in a shop, such beautiful wood! "It's red gum," Jim remembered saying. Looking at it afresh that morning.

Well. Lot of water under the bridge. Jim steadied himself for the trudge down there.

Sunny day. Glaring.

He'd get the paper. Take a headache tablet and have a sit down when he got home. Bolts, for now. Gate bolts. Galvanised. A couple of yards of chain.

There was a point Jim Carlyle knew well when you were pulling up stumps. You dug and chopped and sweated and levered with a jimmy bar until you were sure the damn thing was rooted somehow to a concrete chunk clear through to the other side of the world, but when you finally went and got some chains onto it, or the tractor forks, and you could apply some decent horsepower, you'd feel it finally give. You'd feel the very second the thing gave up the ghost and yielded. A dislocated shift and then a loosening.

He felt it now, or something like it, in the bones in his own head. The sudden cracking headache you sometimes got when you whipped your neck around suddenly to check what you were reversing into; a rip through the shoulder tendons, a blaze and a fade. Like a big electrified hand grabbing your scalp.

He stood and waited for it to clear. Waited for its one compensation— the sudden blotting and receding that came in its wake, which stopped your previous train of thought in its tracks. Neuralgic, the doctors called this pain. Margie had taken all the notes, taken charge of his medication. Now this blankness, like a silent branch dropping, shorting out an electric fence. You wanted that silence rather than the relentless tick of the circuit, taking you down some track to what was waiting for you there. Something big and painful. Some nagging thought or looming memory you'd rather swerve in the dark to avoid.

"Imagine the sequence of thoughts in a certain order, strung together like beads," one of the doctors had said to him and Margie when he'd had the scan, "and you've got to restring the beads." Jim saw, in his mind's eye, beads bouncing and rolling across a floor, disappearing into every corner. Had that happened? One of the girls—Lauren, it was, yes—holding up the cat for a photo, the cat snagging its paw in her necklace, Margie crying out in mock dismay as they'd all jittered and spun away under the furniture. Clutched in Jim's hand now, still, hard little fragments of hurtful memory: Vince losing his job, then getting hit with the cancer stick, and then the wet day of the funeral. He'd gone out to the kitchen to find Margie standing there crying silently, weeping like he'd never seen her. Waiting for the pot on the stove to boil so she could make everyone at the wake a cup of real coffee, the row of tiny cups Vince and Carmela had given her standing on the bench. Margie inconsolable, hunched there ready to switch the pot off as soon as it began hissing, the way Vince had taught her, Margie saying *leave me alone and let me do this*.

Jim had had an inkling then. Some capacity in her he'd never glimpsed. Some secret corner opening up. Bitter fine grounds at the bottom of the cups, and Carmela so obviously a widow now numbly turning that cup like a thimble on its saucer, letting the black brew go cold. All black, that day. Everything black.

He and Vince: lots of fishing, lots of drinking home brews in the shed while their wives thought they were out there making salami, Vince saying *you know, Jim, when I come here I didn't meet one man I could trust, not one.* Then, awkward but still serious: *You a good friend, Jim, you make this OK for me* and Jim cutting him off, saying: *enough of that now, let's have another one.* The shift of things embedded, the scatter of each unthreaded bead. That time they'd turned on the little black-and-white portable TV Vince kept in his shed to watch the soccer—it had been a great day for Vincie the day SBS had started broadcasting—and what had they sat there watching? Jim stared down, now, at the keys in his hand, breathing in and out and waiting for it to fetch itself up from the dark.

Not the footy, not the Cup. Something momentous.

Some footage they kept playing over and over with that moron Reagan making some solemn cowboy speech afterward, a spacecraft, a shuttle, blazing as hot as a ball of sun into Vince's dim shed, arcing up into the sky that got so rapidly dark and Vince saying *Jim, see now, those poor souls, here is where,* then something going wrong, some tiny pinprick of blinding light fizzing, then all that driving momentum faltering, the molten nose of the thing burning clear as day and comet-bright. Big pieces falling away to burn, chunks of tinder floating into empty space. Oh, he could see it now just as clearly, the way it detached itself from its course, piece by piece, discarding huge sections that just drifted aflame back down to earth.

Jim doubted his recollection suddenly—surely it just exploded, that shuttle?—then pushed it out of his mind, because here was the hardware shop with the slate step and plate glass and (yes, let it break away, let it fall away and burn, tumbling and loose) what he needed was a rubber seal for Margie's coffee rocket and the day was glaring white—his foot up onto the step now—and inside there was a man waiting for him to show him trust was possible, a man who had exactly the thing he needed.

See, here was the yield, time just standing waiting for him to muster it all. Threading on, fingers feeling for each one so you could comfort yourself without even looking, there they were in place, each of them strung into decades like a rosary. Those shared Christmas lunches in the heat with paper hats sticking to their damp foreheads and only one beer in case the bushfire alarm sounded and they'd have to jump for the truck. Watching the Boxing Day Test Match and Vince saying *Jim, you will excuse me when I say this, I understand all the rules you tell me for cricket, yes, but this is a fucking slow game* and both of them laughing till they cried. The two of them, Vincent and Carmela, never once saving enough to go back to Italy, and that year Vince got the news his father had died and he came out of the shed to see the table Jim had made them for an anniversary present, big beams of red gum out of the old shearing shed he'd put through his thicknesser till it was smooth as glass and all the grain showed through, and Vince's hand flat upon it, stroking, speechless, and Carmela—a woman Jim had never been able to take his eyes off, his secret, shameful yearning—dipping her fingers into a glass of red wine and shaking drops over the table and the immaculate white embroidered tablecloth she'd spread over it, saying *there, good, now we can eat, now we can start and not be nervous.*

His headache now was something you could sell to science, and in a rosary there was the short strand with the Apostle's Creed, the Lord's Prayer, and the three Hail Marys for faith, hope, and charity, and the large bead still curled hard in Jim's hand, finding its place there, was that moment in the corner of the kitchen where his wife wept *leave me alone and let me do this*, how he'd stood still, unable to comfort her, listening to that rising hiss of the coffee, his heart starting its slow appalled break at that moment; he could see that clearly now, and it was stuck fast and deep in him, this hard, layered secret.

Here, though, he was here now, and Margie waiting for him at home—chair, sandwich, panadol, cool dim living-room—all he had to do was get what he needed in here, then the newsagents for the paper and back to the car, no need to linger in town. He was still standing here under the awning of the hardware store, and as he shifted forward he was taken aback momentarily by the doors opening automatically, something he couldn't remember, and a gust of chilled air coming out. A conjuring trick of a shop. Dimensions the same but packed to the rafters—confoundingly—with anything but hardware. Where the familiar rows of paint cans had always been stacked, Jim stood blinking warily at piled cane baskets and artificial flowers. He walked toward them—a mirage that would clear soon—and his foot struck something. He glanced down, mystified.

Something was wrong, first off, with the solidity of what his boot had just kicked. The thing looked like stone but felt light and hollow, flimsy as a plastic drum, and here they were, at least fifteen of them, all identical. Jim's mind searched through many, many compartments, lightning quick but bone weary, for the name of them. Asian. Big blank face. *Buddha.* Fifteen plastic *Buddhas*.

He reached down, rendered mute with disorientation, and felt the head of the nearest one, his fingers moving wonderingly over the stippled grey surface. Definitely not carved from stone. Plastic. Molded plastic. He rocked the statue back and forth for a moment, smothering panicked, baffled despair. What were they FOR, these things? What were they doing here?

Then snowy static, something big dislodging itself suddenly, a molar torn up and out, the yielding give. The bright drenching.

Here, came Vince's voice, *here is where.*

Something broken loose to drift in burning chunks through the atmosphere, all coordinates failing, and Jim kept going down, his kneecap connecting hard with the floor, too hard, in the fizzing tipping blur he couldn't prevent. The jabbing gouge of the tractor's fork, the chain biting then whipping itself taut and trembling inside his skull.

He still heard everything, clear as day. A couple of customers stopping, leaning over him, voices distant and buzzing like flies on a window ledge, and the young staff members in blue polyester uniforms, one coming out of the storeroom where all those years ago Vincenzo Geroni had put his hand without a second's doubt on the right rubber seal and put it, beaming, into Jim's hand. That man's big heart. He couldn't bear it.

A knot of onlookers now, watching an old man sink to the floor and put his hand flat down on the floorboards like someone genuflecting and reverently touching an altar. *This is red gum,* Jim heard himself say in his own head, but only the side of his mouth seemed to respond, *this floor will last another hundred years.* But the young fella, with the shirt with the yellow $2 logo on it where it should have said 'Peterson's Hardware', looked pale and pinched and indecisive, then he got out his mobile phone without answering, and someone else said, "He doesn't know where he is," and Jim, wincing at the pity in the voice, kneeling on the solid, beautiful timber floor, anchoring himself to the fact of it, could only agree.

From "Drinks with Dead Poets"

No. 1. Keats reads to six in the village hall.

'When old age shall this generation waste,
Thou shalt remain, in midst of other woe
Than ours, a friend to man, to whom thou say'st,
"Beauty is truth, truth beauty,"—that is all
Ye know on earth, and all ye need to know.'

Twelve hands make the sound of ten hands clapping, because Heath doesn't deign to clap from his chair three rows back, he just nods alone in the dark a bit as if that helps. Then again, at least he showed up, to show his tough-guy approval of the gifted little chap. No sign of bloody Orlando or Barry or Lula Lopez. On the front row the angels clap ferociously, Iona McNair, Mrs. Caroline Jellicoe, and a tall girl called Isabella I believe I know. And wordless shy Kevin's clapping for all his worth, as am I, as I sit down next to John on the edge of the stage again, but that's ten hands and that's your lot.

Wonderful, John, you said you'd be happy to take some questions?

(He looks at me and shrugs and Caroline's already raised her hand)

'That was so beautiful, John. Can you tell us something about your influences?'

Influences, John?

(He looks at me as if this wasn't quite what he had in mind, but he seems to make up his mind to be agreeable)

'I—never quite despair if I read Shakespeare.'

(The three women are all nodding in approval, and he goes on) 'I'm very near agreeing with Hazlitt that Shakespeare's enough for us.'

Hazlitt, yes, earlier, John, we met earlier remember, you talked about Dante...that amazing Canto Five of *Inferno*? (I haven't had time to look it up but at least I got the number)

John smiles wider than ever before, his legs give a little dangling kick, and he leans back with his hands spread behind him on the dusty stage: "Paulo and Francesca...I dreamt of—I'd passed many days in rather a low state of mind and I—I dreamt of being in that region of hell…one of the most delightful enjoyments I ever had…I floated about the whirling atmosphere with—with a beautiful figure to whose lips mine were joined—it seemed for an age—I was warm…flowery treetops sprung up and we—we rested on them with the lightness of a cloud…I tried a sonnet but—nothing.'

Did you cry to dream again, John?

He clocks my Caliban, applauds me briefly with a bully-for-you, and says 'I could dream it every night.'

This obviously earns a short adoring silence, which Isabella breaks by asking 'Do you think a poet is born? Or can you learn to be one?'

I glance at her approvingly but she's gazing on him like the moon at a planet. I'm being cold-shouldered in my own coma.

'In the first place,' saith the poet, 'Sancho will invent a journey heavenward as well as anybody.'

From *Don Quixote* there (inserts their teacher).

'No…the poetical character,' goes John, 'it's not itself…'

Isabella's already seriously nodding and scribbling, 'it—*has* no self. It's everything and nothing. It has no character. It enjoys light and shade, it lives in—*gusto*, be it foul or fair, high or low, rich or poor. It has—it has as much delight in conceiving an Iago as an Imogen. A poet is the most *unpoetical* thing in existence, because he has—he has no identity. He's continually in for—filling some other body…'

Are you talking in terms of the poet as playwright, John?

To which he pays no heed: 'I think poetry should—surprise by a—a fine excess, not by singularity. It should strike the reader as a—a wording of his highest thoughts—appear almost a remembrance…its touches of beauty should never be halfway—the rise, the progress, the setting of imagery should—like the sun—come natural to him, shine over him and set soberly, in the—luxury of twilight…' He grins and looks for his water bottle, 'but it's easier to think what poetry should be than to write it.'

Iona has a question: 'Do you have a favourite way to work?'

He's still concluding his thought: 'If poetry comes not as naturally as the leaves to the tree…it'd better not come at all.'

(I say after a silence) Iona's asking if you have a way you tend to work, John.

'Where you sit,' she smiles, 'like a nice view of something? Do you write at dawn? After midnight?'

A lark or an owl, John (I go helpfully); I'm a lark myself if anyone's interested.

'I read and write about eight hours a day…' at which Iona's mouthing to Isabella *oh my Lord*… 'I went day by day at a poem for a month—at the end of which time I found my brain so overwrought I'd neither rhyme nor reason in it—yet…It'd be a great delight to know in what position Shakespeare sat when he began "To be or not to be…"'

He chuckles and points at himself with both forefingers, as if to say How about cross-legged like me? pretends to inscribe verses on the air, and we all laugh, then he goes back to the question, indicating an imaginary room of his dreams, setting out walls and all his special places:

'My books in a snug corner…Mary Queen of Scots…Milton with his daughters in a row…a head of Shakespeare…I should like the window to open onto Lake Geneva, and there I'd sit and read all day like the picture of somebody reading…'

'Can we come and visit?' Caroline Jellicoe beams for England.

'Fine weather, and health, and books, and a fine country,' the young poet sighs, 'a contented mind, a diligent habit of reading and thinking—and an amulet against the ennui, please heaven, a little claret wine cool out of a cellar a mile deep, a rocky basin to bathe in, a strawberry bed to say your prayers in, a nag to go you ten miles or so,' then he gestures to his tiny little audience, 'two or three sensible people to chat with,' then at me with a wink for dramatic counterpoint—'two or three spiteful folks to spar with, two or three odd fishes to laugh at, and two or three numbskulls to argue with!'

John, that's so—

'*And—and—*a little music outdoors played by somebody I don't know…a little chance music…'

He starts engraving on the air again, mouthing the exaggerated shapes of 'To Be Or Not To Be That Is The Question…' when the sweet quiet is abruptly broken by a loud voice from the side of the hall. I look there in time to see big Barry Wilby silhouetted by the light of the porch, only just arriving, having missed the whole of the reading. He repeats himself but louder again:

'Where d'you get your ideas, Mr. Yeats?'

(Oh for fuck's sake) You know what? Let's walk twenty yards with John Keats and bloody well get him his claret wine and his numbskulls! Ladies and gentlemen, I give you John Keats!

No. 5. John Clare crashes the Faculty Reading

It's fair to say I don't know how this happened. At the bright end of the darkened village hall someone's reading to the faculty. It's clearly not Lula's poetry slam, The Night of the Living Living, which would probably have come with red lights and heckles and drunken whoops from the audience—most of whom would be on the bill sooner or later, we've all been there—but there's a murmurous consternation, an undertow of protest. Eight professors are seated on the stage, clinging to or sort of climbing in their chairs, two now standing up, one sat back there grinning till it's over—that's Wayne aka *format* relishing the chaos—because in had walked John Clare, flushed and muddy from his endless walk, and now he's planted there bolt upright in his rags, very loudly reciting—

'Here was commons for their hills where they seek for freedom still,
Though every common's gone and though traps are set to kill
The little homeless miners—O it turns my bosom chill
When I think of old "Sneap Green", Paddock's Nook and Hilly Snow,
Where bramble bushes grew and the daisy gemmed in dew
And the hills of silken grass like cushions to the view,
Where we threw the pismire crumbs when we'd nothing else to do—
All levelled like a desert by the never-weary plough,
All banished like the sun where that cloud is passing now,
And settled here for ever on its brow...'

As Lula Lopez would tell me later at the haven of the Cross Keys bar, 'Titmouse stuck her reading on an *hour* before mine, chief, right, Kerri says bitch said she knew nothing about it, but there's like a shitload of fliers everywhere, so she's lying through her little teeth right, anyhow I go looking for my poets to tell them it's off, so I don't see him coming, and you didn't see him in the fields, chief, did you (you had One Job, etc.) so the bloke must've just seen the lamps and gone right in. He was speaking some poem aloud when he came through the door, he just moseyed up to the stage and carried on speaking. And those wankers didn't know how to stop him.'

They didn't, nor did I. And I wasn't about to, though most likely I'm one too.

I saw Jeff Oloroso rise in the stanza break and make a gentle move toward John Clare, but he wasn't fast enough, and on went the lamentation:

'O I never thought that joys would run away from boys
Or that boys should change their minds and forsake such summer joys,
But alack, I never dreamed that the world had other toys
To petrify first feelings like the fable into stone,
Till I found the pleasure past and the winter come at last—
Then the fields were sudden bare and the sky got overcast
And boyhood's pleasing haunts like a blossom in the blast
Was shrivelled to a withered weed and trampled down and done,
Till vanished was the morning spring and set the summer sun
And winter fought her battle-strife and won...'

Once this stanza had begun, Jeff's smile steadied into place, and he raised his hands as if to say 'why not', then made his slow beaming way along the side of the hall, doing an odd little rhythmic dance with his arms, as if dancing to the beat of the poem, toward me and Samira.

'Oompa oompa, one of your special guests, Glyn?' he didn't whisper.

Uh-huh. Is there a problem?

'Excuse me,' Samira began—

'No problem on earth,' said Jeff, 'he'll be out by midnight though, right? We've got a good few to get through!'

'Excuse me, when will you reschedule Night of the Living Living?' demanded Sami fiercely, but Jeff enquired of me as if she wasn't there: 'We hear you'll be joining us next term?'

That's John Clare there (was all I could think to say).

Jeff glanced at the situation, turned back to me, weirdly put his hand on my shoulder, and said, as if I saw this life as he did, 'Now *he'd* be good in a slam!'

This observation lost him his chance to intercede in the stanza break, during which John Clare had to pause to catch his breath and mop his brow, but now three stood up on the front row. One was Tina Yeager in a pale pink frock and a blue wrap, one a young man in a blazer, saying 'bravo, bravo, nice one to end on,' but Clare wasn't ending *jack*, he was gathering speed over sporadic heckling:

'By Langley Bush I roam, but the bush hath left its hill;
On Cowper Green I stray, 'tis a desert strange and chill;
And spreading Lea Close Oak, ere decay had penned its will,
To the axe of the spoiler and self-interest fell a prey;
And Crossberry Way and old Round Oak's narrow lane
With its hollow trees like pulpits, I shall never see again:
Enclosure like a Bonaparte let not a thing remain,
It levelled every bush and tree and levelled every hill
And hung the moles for traitors—though the brook is running still,
It runs a naked stream, cold and chill...'

During this stanza they tried all sorts—slow-hand clapping, loudly joking, strolling to the buffet to chat about sashimi, and when the break came I saw Mike—my new pal from Human Resources, whom I saw now was one of the three who'd risen from the front row—move to stand there almost blocking Clare from view, more than happy to bring things to a helpful close.

But the third who'd risen I recognized too—not at first, as I hadn't expected to see him here—but when he intervened, seemed almost to bump Mike back to his seat, muttering 'Sit the fuck down, mate, free speech,' it transformed into Heath Bannen. He must have gone there because he's *format*'s student. Mike simply grinned and obeyed, smiling 'very well said, exactly,' and Tina, left standing in her pink dress, had no choice but to sit down too, folding her arms to wait it out.

'O had I known as then joy had left the paths of men,
I had watched her night and day, be sure, and never slept again,
And when she turned to go, O I'd caught her mantle then
And wooed her like a lover by my lonely side to stay,
Ay, knelt and worshipped on as love in beauty's bower,
And clung upon her smiles as a bee upon a flower,
And gave her heart my poesies all cropped in a sunny hour
As keepsakes and pledges all to never fade away—
But love never heeded to treasure up the may,
So it went the common road with decay.'

Now Tina pounced, as if she was counting lines for the break. She couldn't know he'd actually finished the poem—only he and I knew that—but she'd gone quickly to the upright piano, canvas-draped in its shabby corner, smartly plucked the aging flowers from the vase there, and had thrust them into the arms of John Clare before another word was spoken. Not just a pretty face.

'That was such a sweet poem, give it up for our surprise guest!'

Jeff went clapping to the stage to make sure: 'As Tina says, a lovely surprise, that was cool, bro, you're like a rapper with all your rhyming, well done!'

'I think we're thoroughly warmed up now!' Tina declared.

He'd finished anyway (I hissed at her childishly as I reached the scene).

'Any more up your sleeve, Maxwell?'

Come to the pub, John, come to the pub,

John was nodding at the applause because he took it for applause, but he also looked curiously at Heath and Mike and back at Heath and said to them together, though I don't think either one could hear, 'All have liberty to think as they please,' and then up came Lula and Roy Ford from wherever they'd been sitting, and Sami and Heath close by to help me walk him out of there.

This squad of doughty rescuers made a beeline for the Cross Keys, and though I began trying to explain the confusion, I thought better of it, and made the best of where we'd got to:

Brilliant reading, John, but these are the ones I want you to meet!

He was frowning and glancing back at the hall as we crossed the road toward the green lamplight of the Cross Keys. Lula, still bristling at the loss of her main event, spoke up for the gang we were now: 'Tossers in there, mate, you stick with us!'

'Could see it in their faces,' John said to her, or possibly to her cropped scarlet hair he was trying to make sense of, 'Didn't like his looks from the first.'

'Which one, can you narrow it down?' said Sami drily.

'I'm a good physiognomist,' he said more to himself, still holding the dead flowers to his chest.

We got him through the door into the welcome heat, to the snug with the plum-upholstered armchairs, sat him down in the best one by a merrily raving fire, spread ourselves round in the others. Roy and I went for drinks, Lula perched on the arm of his armchair. When we brought our laden trays to the group it had been augmented by Kevin Proctor, deep in a fisherman's blue jumper, and Caroline Jellicoe, whom we hadn't seen all day. Lula was sharing her woes with Clare because they were woes and there he was:

'And you'da been totally welcome mate, you'da totally headlined right?'

John (I began, presenting him with two foaming pints so I could stay there for a while) a lot of my friends here arc just starting out on, you know, the journey, so—d'you remember writing your first poems? Can you tell us about that at all?

He drank and stared at me, sporting a foam moustache, as if sizing up why I was asking. I hoped my face met his physiognomical standards, and began to assume it didn't when he suddenly spoke up:

'I was very timid. Very timid disposition.' He wiped his mouth.

Yes? (The others went silent and leaned in to hear)

'Had, two or three, haunted spots to pass. Impossible to go half a mile anywhere where nothing'd been seen by these, these old women...'

When you were a boy, you mean? You were frightened by—local stories?

He made a little grimace.

'Best remedy to keep such things out of my head, I—muttered over tales of my own fancy, contriving 'em into rhymes as well as I were able...romantic wanderings of sailors, soldiers, step by step...'

Right, right, to take your mind off the ghostly places you were walking through at night? You made up poems to take your mind off—

'Will-with-a-whisp, Jimmy Whisk, Jack-with-a-lanthorn...this November month they're often out in the dark misty nights. Rotten Moor, Dead Moor...'

That's my birthday month for you!

'Melancholy season,' he confided to the girls close by.

November, yup, but you—you cheered yourself up?

'I—loved to see a tale end happy. Intrigues, meeting always good fortune and marrying ladies.'

Lula cackled with joy and her woes were done: 'Were *you* in the stories, though, Mr. Clare?'

'We was not without loves,' he mused to her delight, 'we had our favourites in the village. When a face pleased me I scribbled a song or so in her praise, tried to get in her company.'

He glanced around, but again his eyes fixed on Lula's dyed hair and he seemed very slightly to shake his head, as if processing the peculiar. Then he just as slightly nodded, perhaps thinking some sprite was present and he was noting the phenomenon. I pressed on:

I see this lot writing in the pub, in the café, sometimes walking down the high street, where do *you* like writing, John?

His finger travelled the dust of the table, it seemed to cheer him to remember: 'Always wrote my poems in the fields. Particular spots I's fond of, from the beauty or the secrecy...It's common in villages to pass judgment on a lover of books as—indication of laziness. I was drove to—hide in woods, dingles of thorns in the fields. 'Stead of going out on the green at the town end on winter Sundays to play football, I stuck to my corner, poring over a book...Feelings stirred into praise, and my, my promises muttered in prose or rhyme—grew into quantity. Indulged my vanity in thinking how they'd look in print. Selected what I thought best. Hid the others out of shame's way—laughing-stocks!'

VIET THANH NGUYEN
The Committed

In the morning, before we left, we presented my aunt with a gift from Indonesia, a package of *luwak*, one of four in Bon's duffel. Civet coffee? she said, bemused. We were already savoring cups of coffee at her table, brewed in her coffee press from Arabica beans of her own supply. It's an Indonesian specialty, I said. The civet cat eats the raw coffee beans. Once the cat excretes them, the coffee farmer picks out the beans. The civet's intestines supposedly ferment the beans in a special way. My aunt burst out laughing, which rather hurt me, for luwak was very expensive, especially for refugees like us. We had been inspired by one of the Boss' henchmen, who had approached us, the day before our departure from home, with three packages of luwak as gifts for his patron in Paris. The Boss really loves this coffee, the henchman said. His quivering nose, scraggly whiskers, and black pupils bore some resemblance to the features of the civet pictured on the packages. Boss asked for it special. Bon and I scraped together our money and with these scrapings bought the fourth package of luwak my aunt now held. Oh, the poor farmer! she said, wrinkling her nose. What a way to make a living. But—aware now of her potential faux pas—I'm sure this is delicious. Tomorrow morning I'll brew us a cup—or at least, I'll make one for you and me. She nodded toward me, as by tomorrow morning, Bon should be with the Boss.

Sober in the morning light, Bon thanked her for her hospitality and made no mention of the devil that had divided them the previous night, when he had seen the picture of Ho Chi Minh on her mantel. In his previous life as an assassin for the South Vietnamese army, he would have killed her for such a display. The fact that he could be courteous now was progress, a sign that the City of Light might have cultured him just a touch. We left her apartment and, following her directions, walked a block to the metro stop Voltaire, stopping along the way at a tobacconist's to buy cigarettes and a pair of Cuban cigars to celebrate our arrival in Paris. I conducted the transaction in my grade school French, which was easy enough, for all I had to say was "I would like…" and "thank you," aided by some pointing and an obsequious smile. After having survived a Vietnamese reeducation camp located somewhere in hell's inner circle, and a deserted island somewhere in the middle, and an Indonesian refugee camp in hell's outer fringes, we had finally arrived in the most civilized of places. Here one could simply walk out the door and buy fresh fruit and vegetables at the market, or fresh bread at the baker, or fresh pastries at the pastry shop, or visit the tobacconist for Cuban cigars, which were outlawed in America (where I lived for a time). And whereas in America the average American was the product of an industrial supply chain that led to such girth and heft that he or she dwarfed us Vietnamese, in Paris the people stood at a more modest, artisanal scale. This was true regardless of whether they happened to be white, black, or that other shade I had, up till then, rarely seen in my life, the sand-beige of North Africans or Arabs. Physically, at least, I did not feel out of place as someone not white, or at least off-white, with the mixed heritage given to me by my French father and Vietnamese mother. The eleventh arrondissement was a more mottled version of the Paris recorded in postcards and movies, starring only white people. As with Hollywood's rendering of America as a place populated mostly by white people, save the occasional servant, slave, or sad Indian, this monochromatic wish projection proved that a lie could become a truth for many people.

Even though I heard not a word of English, and saw no signs of tourists on the street or in the depths of the metro, I did not feel out of place. More accurately and paradoxically, while I did feel out of place, that sensation was something I looked forward to. As a bastard, I had been out of place for so long that dislocation felt like the right location to me. Furthermore, I loved to learn, and one did not learn much from feeling at home. Comfort dulled the mind, while a certain measure of homelessness sharpened it. So it was with the metro. Neither Bon nor I had ever ridden a metro or subway before, and the rush of people down the stairways and through the halls was both novel and familiar, for daily life in our homeland was even more of a mad scramble.

The new, subterranean geography disoriented us, but following my aunt's directions and the signs in the metro, we successfully transferred at Nation and again at Place d'Italie before exiting at Porte d'Ivry. Along the way, we marveled at the efficiency of the trains, the lingering scent of urine, and the presence of buskers and hawkers in the stations.

Perhaps we expected the air, even in the tunnels, to be perfumed and the people to be above such menial tasks as scrabbling for a living, in the City of Light. Still, it was not too much of a shock to see Parisians in this way, for we had already lived in Los Angeles, which resembled the so-called Third World more than it did Hollywood's autobiographical fantasies, at least in our déclassé corner of the city.

Now we found ourselves in the thirteenth, the Asiatic Quarter, or Chinatown, of which we had heard many rumors and tales in the refugee camp. There the refugees endlessly discussed the satellites of the homeland to which our countrymen had been transported before us—Berlin, Sydney, Vancouver, and so on. The thirteenth of Paris was second only to Orange County, California, which I already knew too well from my American sojourn. Almost immediately on leaving the metro station we saw the familiar faces of our race, Chinese or Vietnamese from the evidence of the languages they spoke without self-consciousness. Most of these faces were ugly or unremarkable, but nevertheless reassuring. The average person of any race was not a good-looking specimen, but while the ugliness of others only confirmed our prejudices about them, the homeliness of one's own people was comforting. So was the sight of our customs and practices, which were perhaps out of place in the City of Light but nevertheless raised the temperature of our hearts a few degrees. I speak of the way that Asians tended to shuffle rather than step as they walked, and of how the men typically strode ahead of their long-suffering women, who carried all the shopping bags, and of how one of these same examples of chivalry cleared his nose by closing one nostril with a finger and forcibly ejecting the contents through the other, the missile narrowly missing my foot by a foot or two. Disgusting, perhaps, but also easily washed away with the rain, which is more than can be said for a balled-up tissue littering one's way.

Our destination was an import-export store on one of the side streets of Boulevard Leningrad, not far from the Tang Frères supermarket, where we would go later with the shopping list given to us by my aunt. The import-export business announced its intentions with signs using French, Chinese, and Vietnamese: its services included the dispatch to our homeland of parcels, letters, and telegrams, which is to say the delivery of hope itself. Inside, behind the counter, stood floor-to-ceiling shelves stacked with boxes and packages. One of the two clerks attended to the only customer, a dapper silver-haired gentleman in a bow tie and herringbone jacket, who was discussing, in the finest French, the cost of shipping the three boxes on the counter to our homeland. The brand-new boxes bore illustrations of Sony stereos that included speakers, cassette decks, and radio tuners, the kind young people liked to carry out to street corners and parking lots to disturb the peace, and remind the old of their age. You're sure these will get there? the gentleman said. Sure, sure, uncle, the clerk said. What had first appeared to be blush on his cheeks was, on closer inspection, the bloom of acne. We do this all the time, never lost a package. The other clerk looked at us from his stool behind the counter and, by way of greeting, grunted.

I told him I was looking for the Boss. This clerk, without acne but no better-looking than his colleague as a result, said the Boss was not in, just as the henchman had told us he would say. We're the ones from Pulau Galang, Bon replied. He's expecting us. The clerk grunted again, eased himself from his stool with hemorrhoidal care, and disappeared down an aisle of shelves. The clerk with acne handed the dapper gentleman a receipt and began taping labels to the boxes, each one with the same address in Can Tho. Inefficient, no? the gentleman said to me. I'd rather send money but you know what happens to that. I murmured my agreement. He was shipping these stereos home for his relative to sell on the black market, a phenomenon I had witnessed in the months that we had spent in the navigator's house in Saigon, waiting for a boat in order to escape the country. Lucky neighbors would come home with packages from the post office, making them objects of both envy and suspicion, for while those packages afforded them life's necessities, they also marked their recipients as those with blood ties to the refugees from the old regime.

The clerk without acne came back and said, He's waiting for you.

Behind the counter, down an aisle, and through a door was the office, scented with lavender air freshener, its floor decked in linoleum and its walls decorated with pinup calendars featuring Hong Kong models in exuberant poses. October 1985. The Boss stood up from behind his steel desk and came to greet us, and we almost did not recognize him. In the refugee camp, he had been as emaciated and ragged as everyone else, hair shoddy, his one shirt stained brown under the pits and between the shoulder blades, his only footwear a pair of thin flip-flops—in sum, he was a refugee, closer to the Neanderthals than to *homo sapiens*, at least in the eyes of those still classified as *homo sapiens*. Now he was clad in loafers, creased slacks, and a polo shirt, the casual wear of the urban, Western branch of *homo sapiens*, his trimmed hair parted so neatly one could have laid a pencil in the groove. In our homeland, he had owned considerable interests in rice, soda pop, and petrochemicals, not to mention certain black market commodities. After the revolution, the communists had relieved him of his excessive wealth, but these overeager plastic surgeons had sucked away too much fat from this fat cat. Threatened with death by starvation if he stayed, he had fled, survived, and come here, needing only a year to become a businessman again and reassume the padded appearance of humanity.

We commenced our masculine social grooming ritual by embracing and slapping each other on the back. Bon and I assumed the position of the socially inferior simians by offering him the tribute of the three packages of luwak provided by his henchman. Then the fun began, which involved smoking French cigarettes and drinking calvados from snifters. The type and mode of imbibing indicated the Boss' sophistication, for in our homeland the drink of manly choice was the more conventional cognac, cut with soda and ice, in highball glasses. When we remarked that we had never taken him for the type to appreciate coffee brewed from the beans defecated by a civet, he gave his best imitation of a smile, picked up a letter opener, slit open one of the packages, and shook out a gleaming brown bean onto his palm, where it glistened under the light of his desk lamp.

I don't drink coffee, he said. Tea, yeah, but coffee's too strong.

We looked at the poor bean, the tip of the letter holder pressed against its belly. The Boss rolled the bean with his fingers until it ended up between his thumb and index finger, and then scraped it gently with the letter opener's blade. The brown came off in flakes, like paint, revealing whiteness underneath. Not that you really need to take the color off, he said. It's just vegetable dye. Won't hurt you, even up the nose. He opened the second bag, shook out another bean and scratched off a portion of the coloring again to reveal the whiteness beneath. Got to check the product, he said. You can't always trust the henchmen. Matter of fact, rule of thumb, never trust the henchmen. He opened a drawer and took out a hammer, as if hammers should always be kept in desk drawers. The bean, when tapped with the hammer, crumbled into a fine powder. He dabbed a finger in the white powder, tinged with the brown, and licked it. My brief glimpse of his pink tongue made my big toe twitch. Sniffing's the best test, he said. But I got people for that. Or you could do it. Want a try?

We shook our heads. He offered another facsimile of a smile and said, Good boys. Then he slit open the third bag, shook out another bean, laid it on the desk, and tapped it with the hammer—once, twice, a third time. The bean did not crumble. He frowned and tapped it again a little harder, but with the same result. Then he smashed the bean with a blow that made the desk lamp jump in surprise, and when he lifted the head of the hammer from the table, we saw not fine white powder but instead a circle of debris, all the bits brown to the core. Shit, Bon muttered. You said it, the Boss said, laying the hammer gently down on the desk. He reclined in his chair, the corner of his lips crinkling just a little, as amused as an auditor discovering a cheat's fatal error. Hey, guys, he said. I think we got a problem.

And by we, he of course meant you, or us.

It was reputed that the Boss had a name, but no one knew what it was, or if they did, no one dared utter it aloud. Presumably his father and mother had known his name, but he was an orphan, and perhaps they had never given him a name before throwing him over the wall of the orphanage. The sisters of the orphanage christened him, but no one was certain which orphanage it was. He had run away from it at twelve, no longer willing to tolerate the Catholic lessons, the repetitive diet of porridge with a few flakes of dried pork, the abuse from his fellow orphans for being Chinese, the unending rejection of never being adopted. But without a name or ancestry or papers, and only a few months old, how was it possible that anyone could have recognized this baby as Chinese? Because of the way he looked. His pale skin, his angular eyes, his round face—his fellow orphans knew a Chinese when they saw one, and the sisters had to agree that it seemed likely, if mysterious, for the Chinese were reluctant to give away boys. What had happened, everyone eventually agreed, was that he was not only an orphan but illegitimate. This was why the Boss was so kind toward orphans, and why a good number of his henchmen were themselves orphans, rescued by the Boss or given to the Boss by mothers and fathers who had heard of his reputation.

At the same time, rumor had it that several children throughout Saigon bore a strong resemblance to him, born from other men's wives or from unwed mothers. Despite being an orphan himself, he refused to see or support any of these illegitimate offspring. This behavior was not surprising, at least to him. Like many people, perhaps all people, his true self was built like a submarine, cruising in the vast waters of his consciousness, emerging from the depths only in occasional moments, unknown not only to others but even often to himself. Not knowing oneself was as crucial to survival as knowing oneself, a delicate balance maintained through ballast and bulkheads, and, in times of mortal crisis, the sealing of chambers where those who must die were drowned for the sake of the living, a decision he had made more than once. So it was with any possible children. It was only people who could not make anything themselves who longed for children, wanting a creative power that they had not earned. He had no need for a legacy beyond the legacy he made for himself, the only kind worth having.

While his body had two eyes, like most people, his self saw through the world through the one eye of its periscope. His focused tunnel vision was both strength and weakness, for while he could take his time studying others unobserved, he lacked peripheral vision. Through that periscope, he studied the two sitting before him and decided that they – that we—were not the kind to steal a relatively small sum. A very large sum, yes, anyone would do that if given the chance. But they were not dumb enough to risk their profitable relationship with him over the short-term gain of half a kilogram of cocaine—unless they were addicts, in which case logic was no longer a part of the equation. He knew their predilection for alcohol and cigarettes, but for the many months he had known them, first on the boat, then on the island, and then at the camp, it had been difficult to get access to even those two drugs, much less anything illegal or more damaging, except for paint thinner and glue, so effective at erasing memory and brain cells. Listening to their excuse, he decided that it was possible for them to have accidentally given his luwak to the crazy bastard's aunt. He wondered if the aunt was beautiful, or at least acceptable, if she was heavy or thin, if she wore skirts or pants, if she was a challenge or easy. Spinsters, he knew from experience, were usually both, easy to seduce but challenging to maintain, being so particular and high-strung. Thinking about spinsters made him smile inside. He had long ago severed the connection between what he felt inside and what he showed outside, but that smile made him think about what kind of expression he should offer to the pair in front of him. He reminded himself of what a smile looked like, drew it on his face for them to see, and said, Tell you what. Come back tomorrow with the other bag of luwak. No big deal, right?

They said yes, knowing that it was, in fact, a big deal. People who knew him always said yes, if that was what he wanted, or no, if that was what he wanted. As for people who did not know him, he regarded it as his task to let them know who he was and how they should respond. These two knew him, and understood that if he could not trust them with half a kilogram he could not trust them with anything. He drew the smile on his face again, wrote two addresses down on a piece of paper and gave it to the man with one eye, the only man he knew at the moment for whom he felt a touch of fear, and told him to go there for employment and a residence. They finished their calvados, shook his hand, and left him alone with the cocaine, the bottle of calvados, the packet of cigarettes, a dirty ashtray, three empty snifters, and the hammer. He brushed off the cocaine and coffee smeared on its head and, holding the hammer in his hand, admired its weight, balance, and elegance. He had bought it in a hardware store soon after arriving in Paris, along with a box of nails. Wherever he went, one of the first things he liked to buy or steal, if he didn't already have it, was a hammer. A hammer might be a simple tool, but it was the only thing he had ever needed, besides his own mind, to change the world.

GUNNHILD ØYEHAUG
Eye Blister

Translated by Kari Dickson

She has to get the asylum seeker back to the church. She found him wandering around in the woods behind the church, he'd had enough, he tried to tell her in a language she couldn't understand, but she knew that was what he was trying to say, all the same; he was pale, with big bags under his eyes, and his eyes were bloodshot. His hair, which was dark, lay pressed against his head in two big waves, as though he'd been walking back and forth in the church cellar with his hands clasped over his head, fingers locked. She couldn't believe her luck, that she, who never won anything, had had the good fortune to bump into the asylum seeker in the woods, when he was the very reason she had gone there and aimlessly pulled bark off some random trees in the pretense that she was collecting larch branches for an advent wreath, which was what she'd told Torstein, her husband, she was going to do, whereas in fact she just hoped to catch a glimpse of the asylum seeker in the church.

He was, despite the strange hairdo, extremely attractive, masculine and desperate as he was right now. In fact, she had to admit he was generally incredibly attractive. Could that be the reason she'd become so fascinated with his fate—after she'd read about him in the local paper, an interview with the asylum seeker, who'd had his application turned down and therefore sought sanctuary in the church, and the photograph of a man sitting on one of the hard church pews, his tortured face framed by dark, curly hair, which just wouldn't leave her mind asleep or awake? Could that be why she constantly found herself circling the church in the hope that she would see him in the cellar, where he slept on a mattress? No, surely not.

She has for a long time, before reading about the asylum seeker in the newspaper, been obsessed with Peeta Mellark in *The Hunger Games*; Peeta Mellark replaced Edward Cullen in *The Twilight Saga*, who had in turn taken over from Aragorn in *The Lord of the Rings*. She feels that she's finished with Aragorn and Edward Cullen, they no longer make her slip into a daydream, but Peeta Mellark, on the other hand, he's still kind of new, even though he's like the other men, in the sense that they're all good and intelligent, and most important, incredibly kind—they are goodness incarnate—and she believes in them; even though they're only fictional characters, they seem real; in fact, it's almost impossible to believe that Peeta Mellark doesn't exist. His fair hair, which is sweaty and damp at the neck as he sits up on the sand in the fictitious world of *The Hunger Games*, where they're being held captive in order to entertain the evil president and thrill-seeking population by killing each other until there's only one left: she wants to watch it again and again, it's as though his hair is everything she's longed for, all her life. She wants Peeta Mellark to exist.

She freezes the shot where he looks up at his great love, Katniss Everdeen, who is the heroine and runs around in the forest with a bow and arrow and saves everyone; again and again she watches the moments when his feelings are so apparent on his face, especially the moments when he first looks away and then directly at Katniss, all his longing and all his hopes there just under the skin of his strong jaw, and in his eyes that seem to say, can't you see me, here I am and I love you and will always love you. She looks for interviews with the actor on YouTube; fans have cut together Peeta Mellark moments like this, moments that make your stomach lurch, when Peeta turns, comes into a room. And sometimes when she's at work in the bookshop, she goes to the toilet and finds one of these video mashups and watches it while she sits on the loo, or maybe she doesn't even sit, she just stands against the wall and watches it, and then flushes even though she hasn't peed. She's also watched all the interviews she can find with the actor who plays Peeta Mellark, but they're not as good. It's almost as though Peeta's not there. And the interviews with him and the girl who plays Katniss Everdeen are equally disappointing, they're not in love at all in reality, they're just two young, chatty adults who have nothing to lose, no sisters to save, no worlds in danger of collapsing, and even though she sees that lots of fans have made videos where they've cut together moments from the countless interviews they've done together to find even the tiniest sign that they're maybe in love in real life too, she doesn't think so.

She watches the films over and over again, when Torstein is out jogging, and if he catches her, he shakes his head in exasperation and says, Ellen, you're twenty-seven, those films are for teenagers, and she argues that they're films that can touch anyone, at any age, they have something important to say. And then Torstein takes away the bag of sour jelly sweets that she always likes to eat when she's watching films, and then he says: and you should stop eating sour sweets all the time, it's not good for you. And he's right. She gets little blisters in her mouth from them. Small, white blisters on her gums, which don't bulge out, but are more like small white tunnels in her gums, with a shiny membrane over the top, as though they're eating their way in.

She sometimes dreams about them, she dreams that they appear elsewhere on her body, not just her mouth; for example, she dreams that she's in a shop and is about to pay, she takes the money out of her purse and reaches over the counter, then she notices her hands—the skin is perfectly normal, perhaps a little suntanned, but there's a small, white, shiny spot on her hand, a gum blister, and then she sees one on the other hand as well. But every time she gets these blisters, she thinks, *I can put up with it,* because it reminds her that she saw Peeta Mellark the day before.

The asylum seeker has almost replaced Peeta Mellark, she's thought about him more and more, read the interview over and over again, studied the photograph. And he's actually here, right where she lives, in the church. She's wondered how he survives in the church cellar, she shudders when she thinks of the church cellar, where they used to go for their confirmation classes, where she sat and basically felt like a hypocrite, and her hypocrisy felt solid, not just a vague feeling, but real hypocrisy, as filling and real as an almond slice, she knelt down, she bowed down to the others, it would be too embarrassing to be the only one who didn't get confirmed; she could remember the smell of the plaster, she could feel the green, worn woven fabric on the chairs in the church cellar against her hands when she imagined sitting down to have a cup of tea with him, she could feel the varnished wooden table against her arms, she can hear the sound of the metal mechanism they use to lock the tables together in rows clink when he bumps the table with his thigh as he sits down, with a cup of tea, and looks up at her, and is beautiful and dark and in love, with her, and his intense eyes, in all the chaos and mystery of his life, whereas she, where she sits opposite him, represents freedom.

The feeling is so strong, when she thinks about it, she's almost moved to tears; the feeling of understanding and the desire to protect and save is so intense she feels as though she's part of some kind of cosmos when she thinks about the asylum seeker, she feels she is the ground on which he can walk, she feels that *she,* where she is sitting or will be sitting, on the other side of the table in the church cellar, is the place where the church cellar ends, outside, she is the point where the world starts, she is the asphalt on the path, she is the grass that leads down to the river that swings round the church, and then she is the river, and then she is the ditch on the other side of the river, and then she is the wall and then the road, and then she is the whole world beyond that. She is the air, the light, all the sounds from everywhere. She is freedom. That is what she is. In relation to him, an asylum seeker who has taken refuge in a church, trapped in all the churchiness, with the woven tapestries on the walls, the knotted tapestries with biblical motifs, with the photographs of everyone who has been confirmed here from the 1940s to the present day, rows and rows of grave confirmation faces along the corridor, and perhaps his only daily contact is with the verger, the sexton, and the minister.

She's tried to imagine it, and she's shuddered every time. Not because they're nasty in any way, they're just churchy. She's always felt uncomfortable with anything churchy, and this was only reinforced by the confirmation classes precisely because she felt such a hypocrite. But sometimes, like when they were singing Christmas carols in church, she got a kind of fizzy feeling when she saw how high the roof was and the space felt so open and mystic at the same time, and the burning candles and the picture of Jesus with the nails through his hands and feet, and she felt gratitude, and because she had such a developed sense of empathy, she could almost say that she sometimes felt the nails in her hands, a few times, just a faint tickling in the middle of her palms, a kind of suction pulling inward, but she mustn't think about it too much, she often had to clasp her hands to avoid thinking about it, because then she would remember that awful time during the confirmation course, at one of the services they had to attend: suddenly she started to cry, and her classmates, who were sitting there reading the magazines that they'd hidden inside the Bible, wondered what was wrong, and she'd said that she could feel the nails through her palms, and at the time, she really could feel it, it hurt, and there had been a great kerfuffle, they'd had to usher her out, she was nearly hysterical, and no one believed her, and to this very day she doesn't know why she did it; some people said it was because they had just learnt about Francis of Assisi, the first person to experience stigmata, and that she'd thought about it too much, the fact that you could experience someone else's pain so intensely that blood appeared in the very places that the nails had been hammered in, that she'd imagined that she had also experienced it. Stigmata. She'd overheard one of her teachers saying to another teacher that she had a very vivid imagination, a little too vivid perhaps, and what about that short story she'd written that they had discussed in the staffroom, which could indicate that she was struggling with mental health issues, about the girl who was kidnapped and then actually *killed*, it could be that everything had just tipped over for her in the church, she wasn't exactly easy and didn't really fit in, and they'd been worried about her, they'd noticed she was always on her own in the breaks, and then she wrote the story about the girl who was *killed*, perhaps all the crying in the church had been a way of getting attention, and she heard the other teacher, who was a woman, say that it was certainly a method you could use if you wanted to seem *special* and get *sympathy*, then Ellen turned and walked the other way, so she wouldn't hear any more, but she had felt it, the nails in the palms of her hands, she was convinced of that, at least; but what had made her cry and get hysterical, that was still a mystery to her.

At times, she's thought it was just because she'd seen herself and the situation from the outside, that somehow it changed from being just a vague feeling, sucking inward from the palm of her hand, and a few tears, to the class's reaction, one of the girls in the class who she really wanted to be friends with, but realized that she didn't want it back—just one look from her over the top of the Bible that was hiding her magazine, one look at the tears on her cheeks, a look that said EVERYTHING THAT WE ARE AND YOU'RE NOT, that made her feel naked, that made her just click, that made her weep buckets, and what had been painful was now actually painful, in her hands, her chest, but, she thought, all the same, that the pain in her hands wasn't a real feeling, the thing with her hands, it definitely wasn't stigmata, it *was* an imagined, empathic feeling, and it wasn't smart. She felt tainted by it for a long time after; *that's the girl who thought she felt Jesus' nails through her hands.*

She read up on Francis of Assisi. She had a children's book about him, where he was drawn in a brown monk's robe, with a ring of hair around his head, which was bald on top. He wore sandals and was standing, talking to some birds, and his face was ever so gentle. She didn't like the illustrations, she had never liked the book, she didn't like his tonsure, she didn't like his too gentle face, it made her impatient, when she'd read it as a child, it always made her think of smelly feet, eggs that had been boiled for too long and were green, of pants that were too small, of having wet knees, but Francis of Assisi cared for others, he stood by the sick and especially the lepers who no one else wanted to help, no one can deny him that, not even his hairdo. She read it again, and sat in the library and read about him in the encyclopedia; Francis of Assisi, she said out loud in the religion class, which set her classmates giggling, was she really going to do this, a year later, had she really chosen Francis of Assisi as her subject for Christianity?

Francis of Assisi was the son of a merchant, she said, Francesco, or Francis, as he was called, was one of the many children born to Pietro Bernardone, a rich textile merchant, and his wife, Pica (she'd forgotten to change the encyclopedia's words into her own here, in which case she would have said, Pica, his wife), who came from an aristocratic Italian family living in Provence. He was originally christened Giovanni, she said, as she surveyed the classroom and all the faces that were now in ninth grade with her, and that were staring at her, aghast, but fit to burst, when were they going to be able to laugh, out loud, when was it going to come? But, she said, his father changed it to Francis. Francis was not particularly interested in school. As a youth, he led a very high-spirited life and was rebellious. He was, above all, interested in the modern art of the troubadour, troubadour! someone shouted from over by the window, Jesus, what's that, you know we don't use words like that in here, the teacher said, OK, fine, I won't use the word *troubadour* again, the boy by the window said, and everyone laughed; be quiet and listen to Ellen, the teacher said; well, he was interested in the art of the troubadour, Ellen repeated, and to be honest, partied a lot, much to the annoyance of the rest of the town. But then he fought in a war that ended in defeat for Assisi, and Francis spent a whole year in a miserable prison cell in Perugia and when he was freed he was very ill and nearly died, Ellen read from her papers. Being in that cell nearly killed him. And this, she said, is where you can find the first seeds, but very few of those who have studied or written about Francis of Assisi have given it much thought, she said. Because it was after his imprisonment in this miserable cell that he had his great conversion, his epiphany, if you like. In 1215, he visited a very poor church and listened to a sermon. The priest didn't have the means to buy food, or to put oil in the lamps or to maintain the church. In the semidarkness, Francis knelt down by the altar, Ellen said, with an old Byzantine crucifix (she didn't know what Byzantine meant, so read it slowly and loudly to make it sound like she did), and he started to pray. And it was then that he heard Christ speaking to him from the crucifix he was holding in his hands, telling him to rebuild God's crumbling house. And so he did. But the point is, everyone knows that if you hear someone talking to you from a crucifix, then you're at most semiconscious. You're dreaming, she said. If, Ellen continued, you had experienced the extreme physical and mental strain that being locked in a miserable cell for a long time must entail, then I'm sure you wouldn't react if a crucifix suddenly started talking to you. In other words, it's an illusion, the imagined voice in the crucifix. His conversion was therefore based on an illusion. She avoided looking at the teacher when she said this, she just kept her eyes on her classmates, who now looked as though they didn't know how to react and were staring at the teacher. And then the whole thing became farcical, she said, when he later experienced the stigmata, for which he is so famous, she said and felt the blood vessel on her neck pulsing; as you know, Francis of Assisi was the first person to experience stigmata, on the 14th of September 1224, to be precise, but I haven't managed to find out at exactly what time, but he is said to have been stigmatized on Mount La Verna, and he had the wounds for the rest of his life, which was only another two years anyway. The problem is that the story of his stigmata doesn't appear in the oldest accounts of his life, nor was it mentioned when Pope Gregory IX canonized Francis in 1228. Ellen had no idea what she was talking about now and hoped that she wouldn't get any questions; she just hoped that her conclusion would make them forget the detail: Thus there is much to indicate, she said, that the pope was skeptical of the stigmata story, which had never happened before in history, and even though there have been several occurrences since, this has, if you ask me, also been the result a vivid imagination. But the point is that the pope, who at first didn't believe it and didn't include him in the list of saints, was later convinced in a dream. And then somehow it became true, when the pope put his faith in it. But he only understood it in a dream. That's how it was in the old days. People received things in dreams, had a so-called vision and took it for the god-given truth. Thus, we can conclude: nothing of what we believe we know about Saint Francis of Assisi and the mystery regarding stigmata is true. The truth is that he was a good, kind man who kissed the hands of lepers and all that, which is enough in itself, really. Thank you, she said, and went back to her place.

And just then the door burst open and Torstein, a boy from the parallel class who she had noticed because he had almost white hair, shouted: Fire! And there was, in fact, a fire, or that is to say, while she had been talking about why everything we knew about Francis of Assisi was probably based on a dream and why Francis' own religious epiphany was based on the brain's way of dealing with intense physical and mental strain, in other words by imagining things, a fuse had blown in the plug for the fridge in the canteen, resulting in huge amounts of smoke on the ground floor, and so everyone had to evacuate.

But Ellen had stayed sitting in her place while all the others piled out, and possibly because Torstein felt in some way responsible for getting people out, because he was the one who had come to warn them, he stood there waiting until everyone had left, and when he saw Ellen sitting at her desk staring into thin air, as though she had frozen, as though she thought she could just sit through the fire, he ran over to her, pulled her up, opened the window and pushed her out, then jumped out himself. The fire was quickly extinguished, there was not really much more than smoke, and Torstein and Ellen got married five years later when they were twenty-one; they felt they were connected in some way, which apparently often happens when people are caught in an emergency situation, and now she works in the bookshop and he works in the fish farming industry.

Torstein has never been told that he burst in at the moment she had bowed to the class and tried to disassociate herself from the very thing she believed in most in life, namely imagination, in order to fit in, to prove that she was over and done with the nails in her hands, and now they live an ordinary life, a very ordinary life, and Torstein is happy and thinks it will soon be time to have children, in fact, it has been for a while now, he's often thought to himself while he's out running, on his usual running days, that it's now high time to have children, he loves her; sometimes he sees her like she was that day at school when he almost lifted her from her desk and threw her out the window, how distant she was, how beautiful she was, how utterly herself she was sitting there in the midst of all the confusion, as if for the first time he saw someone who was both alone and unique, whereas Ellen has, for a long time, perhaps all her life, lived in the semidarkness or half-light of day of someone who always dreams of something else.

And now she's actually here, in the woods outside the church, with the asylum seeker. He's almost frightening close up. It's obvious that he's desperate. He shouldn't be out here, it could be catastrophic. She balls her hands and holds them out in front of her, then clasps one wrist with the other hand to symbolize handcuffs, as she looks up at him with an expression that's meant to say, don't you realize, you'll get caught if you're outside the church, and points down to the church, so he'll understand. With synchronized zigzag movements she draws a Christmas tree with her hands and then wiggles her index finger back and forth; as far as she can remember they haven't declared a Christmas amnesty this year, as they have in the past, when asylum seekers who have sought refuge in a church can walk around outside the church without any danger of being detained. She makes the handcuff movement again. Then she thinks that maybe it seems as though she's trying to say that she understands, that he feels chained to the church, she decides to change tactic, she puts her hand on her chest and says her name: ELLEN. It's so strange, she doesn't hear her name when she says it, it's like she's saying E-EN at the back of her throat, it's rather alarming, *why*, she tries again, to articulate with her mouth and tongue E L L E N, now her name sounds thin and reedy, she can't say her name, she gives up. And then she points at him, generously, now you have to say your name, as though he were a child, but he just looks at her furiously, spits on the ground, there is something ferocious about his face, and she thinks his hair is so striking, the two black wings of hair, and oddly they remind her of the way she couldn't say her name, she doesn't understand.

She points tentatively to the church and takes a few steps toward it. He falls to his knees on the moss, you'll get wet, she says, but she doesn't think he understands what she's saying. She tries to remember his name, but she's never managed to read it correctly, it's so long. She can see quite clearly the newspaper article about him and can picture his long name, it starts with A, she tries and tries to read it, but it evades her every time. She gets down on her knees beside him. She feels it so strongly: that she loves him, that this figure kneeling on the wet moss in a wood by a church in Norway, this is all hers, or it's *significant*, it's as though the woods are humming all around them, as though something is going to happen; she gets the feeling that she can control it, she can control the wind, and the soughing in the trees, and that he will look up at her now, and he does, he looks up at her, he does what Peeta Mellark does, almost in slow motion, first he looks away and then he looks up into her eyes, and their faces are so close, and then he leans in toward her, she knows that he's going to kiss her now, but instead with a swift movement he pinches the eyelid of his right eye and pulls it out so the eyeball is visible, and on the bloodshot eyeball, she sees a small white spot, whiter than the eyeball, and she immediately knows what it is, it's a blister, it's a gum blister, the unexpected gum blister on his eyeball seems to dig deeper and deeper into her consciousness, and that's because she's dreaming, until she sinks into something white, unbelievable, shiny. She wakes up, she realizes that she's sitting on the sofa, Torstein is standing over her, looking at her strangely: huh, he says, that's odd, I'm sure I heard you say your name in your sleep, you said e-en, twice, he laughs, he's eating a hotdog with fried onion, do you want one, he asks.

Hotel Majestic

Illusions are art, for the feeling person,
And it is by art that we live, if we do.
—Elizabeth Bowen, *The Death of the Heart*

I.

Ora Fitz breakfasted on the terrace, her manner chaste, irreproachable. She scarcely inclined toward her food, showed small appetite and, afterward, dabbed her mouth with a pressed napkin, leaving suggestive traces of a costly matte lipstick named "Marie." Below, on Via Veneto, traffic was sparse, sidewalks empty.

Boxwood topiaries edged the formal terrace, scented jasmine frothed in white waves over the hotel's pale gold and bisque walls. Waiters in black-and-white uniform stood idle. Beneath Ora's chair, a charcoal-gray pigeon, obdurate and fat, waited for crumbs. Others fluttered from mature plane trees lining the boulevard to the stone parapet or marched across the marble floor with its white-and-black chessboard pattern. Someone breakfasting near Ora spoke to someone else. "We were middle-class families, two servants apiece. After the war, we thought we would return to that. Now, only Eastern Europeans remember the art of service."

The art of disguising loneliness has never left us, Ora thought, uncreasing her hotel map with its garish frieze of advertisements, checking off sites she'd visited, circling the few left to see. Museo Nazionale Etrusco, Palazzo Doria Pamphilj, Galleria Borghese, and Nino's, a famous restaurant near the Spanish Steps. Places that Giles, before he died, had chosen for them to see together.

It was early August, with Rome suffering its worst heat wave in decades. "Scorching," "oppressive," "sizzling," "deadly,"—*Il Messaggero*, the city's newspaper, strained for adjectives. Locked into prepaid bookings, winter dreams of a Roman holiday now mocking them, tourists edged miserably along shady sides of streets, some risking fines to wade, thigh-deep, into the city's famous fountains. "I tip my hat to you," the Pope had said on Sunday to the crowd gathered beneath his window. He didn't tip a hat, he wore no hat, but he did praise his flock's courage, awaiting his papal blessing in such heat. Ora had been there, pasty beneath a cheap Nile green umbrella she'd bought from a hawker, his canvas quiver jammed with polyester and bamboo umbrellas made in China. The Pope withdrew from his window, waving his hand, a cuckoo breathed back into its Black Forest clock.

After breakfast, Ora climbed two flights of marble stairs, forty-four steps, forty-four brass wands holding a continuous stripe of claret carpeting in place. The second-floor hallway was a long, chandeliered curve, white walls hung with oversize black-and-white photographs in gold frames—film stars and directors from the '50s and '60s—Sophia Loren, Virna Lisi, Gina Lollobrigida, Roberto Rossellini, Federico Fellini filming Marcello Mastroianni in *La Dolce Vita*—all taken during the Majestic's heyday, its prime. With a silk-tasseled key, she opened the lacquered white door. Her room had been cleaned, the single bed made. Above its taut snowiness hung four gold-framed prints, architectural sketches by Michelangelo. Floor-length drapes, stately folds of vermilion velvet girdled with gold cording, framed the window; the view was of a private garden of palms, magnolia trees, spires of dark cypress behind a low stone wall. Even with sunlight piercing the green foliage, the view was dull, a faint brushstroke in an ambitious painting, a piece of puzzle, edge or background, its shape similar to a hundred others.

Earlier that morning, Ora had unlatched the white shutters, pushed open the window. Below her, parked opposite on the narrow street was a tiny bright orange car, comically shaped—a brimless bowler. A man sat behind the wheel, his features indistinct. He wore a dress shirt the child's blue of a summer sky. Ora stared, drawn to the car's candy shock of color before she realized she was naked. *Jaybird!* Jerking shut the windows, latching the shutters, she stood paralyzed by embarrassment.

We believe what we like, not always what is true, and one thing we like believing is that we are fairly certain of who we are, a somebody shaped by habits, principles, ideals, others' expectations, cultural constraints, genetics, fears, desires, and so on. Complex, but predictable. Alone in a once-grand hotel, alone much of the time, no longer visibly grieving—it had been two years—Ora Fitz cracked the shutter to gaze a second time at the orange car and, as she did, was seized by an impulse, a compulsion, to expose herself. Like the story she'd heard about a man who, deciding to walk across a famous bridge, got halfway across when he was overtaken by an urge to leap so strong he'd been forced to drop to his hands and knees and crawl to the opposite side to save himself, her urge to pose naked in a hotel window and exhibit herself to a stranger in a parked vehicle was overwhelming. Irresistible. It was also completely out of character.

In this fuguelike state, Ora reopened the shutters, the window, feeling the air, cool at this hour, washing over her large, pale breasts. The sexual arousal was immediate. As she stood naked in the window's frame, a woman in a business suit walked her white Pomeranian, pink ribbons tied to its ears, past the stranger's car.

Ora withdrew, selected clothing from her suitcase, returned to the window. Bordered by vermilion drapes, she staged a dumb show. Cotton panties and bra, print blouse, modest skirt, sandals, a dotted silk scarf in her hair.

Accompanied by her newly excited self, Ora Fitz went downstairs to breakfast.

II.

In a seventeenth-century courtyard off Via del Corso, with its square of parched lemon trees, withered fruit, and dry fountain, Ora found the ticket window, purchased her ticket and audio guide, and climbed several flights of marble stairs to Palazzo Doria Pamphilj. Pressing the device to her ear, she listened as Prince Doria Pamphilj himself told of his idyllic childhood growing up in the palazzo (his privileged voice already grating on Ora's nerves), adding that he still lived here, in a set of private apartments. *Oh, lucky him.* She progressed, accompanied by sparkling bits of Haydn (composed during the Austrian musician's visit to the palace) through a series of enormous, empty staterooms, high-ceilinged, opulent—the Jupiter, the Poussin, the Throne and Velvet Rooms, the Hall of Mirrors. In the Ballroom, she stood near a trio of headless wire mannequins outfitted in the Doria Pamphilj family's original livery—the fabric, green silk and red velvet, faded and rotting—and listened as the Prince related a charming story of being punished as a boy for roller skating back and forth across the ballroom's original sixteenth-century brick floors, hand-cleaned and buffed, as they had been for centuries, with soap, water, and natural beeswax. Ora was deeply interested. What had been *le petit prince's* punishment? His adult voice, smug, silky, pious, provoked vicious envy in her. She imagined stuffing the audio guide and going in search of the Prince's private apartments. His beast hunted down by her beauty. But she was no beauty, and the question of his bestiality, absence or presence, was unknown.

Tireless, the Prince guided Ora, suggesting where she should stand next, what she might gaze upon and why. Absolved of decision, relieved of thought, she stood before paintings by Bruegel, Caravaggio, Fra Filippo Lippi, Raphael, Carracci, and Titian, then entered a mint-green chamber with its famous portrait of Pope Innocent X by Velásquez, a likeness supposedly so true and unflattering it had horrified the Pope when his own pocked and homely face, vivid with avarice, was presented to him. *"Troppo vero!"* "All too true!" he is said to have exclaimed. Safe to assume, Ora thought, people do not care for truth. Perhaps art sprang from a human need to escape truths? What was the tired joke? Mortality—the death of us.

Preserved in the family *capella*, beneath the altar and inside a crystal and rosewood coffin, lay the sinewy corpse of St. Theodora, early martyr of Rome. The Prince, increasingly chummy in Ora's ear, explained that the oldest, most powerful families of Rome had kept one relic, preferably the body of a saint, in their private chapels. Not to be outdone, the Doria Pamphilj family acquired two relics, the second the corpse of the Roman soldier who had stood beneath Jesus' cross. The Centurion, as he was called, underwent a change in destiny when a female member of the Doria Pamphilj family obtained papal permission to bring him with her, for protection, whenever she traveled. It occurred to Ora, peering about the chapel, unable to locate the Centurion (Out traveling? On loan?), that Giles' memory was a sad relic she dragged everywhere, protection and impediment.

The air in these mirrored galleries and shadowy staterooms was stifling, tenebrous with the odored weight of old acquisition. Tall louvered shutters, slightly open, gave little relief. Not far from the Velásquez portrait, a security guard in rumpled white shirt and black pants sat reading a paperback. What if he was Prince Doria Pamphilj, disguised for amusement? One peril of wealth and title would be boredom.

At the tour's end, Ora turned in her audio guide (she heard the Prince, between tinkling bits of Haydn, repeating himself) and left the parched, birdless courtyard, the empty fountain. Out on Via del Corso, the heat's intensity disoriented her. Tourists, schools of glum, sweaty fish, knocked past; it became impossible not to feel misanthropic. People who lived in the city had fled to mountain retreats or seaside idylls; anyone still here was dependent on tourism or too poor to leave. Emptied of its citizens, Rome was overrun by foreign visitors with credit cards, selfie sticks, vague, rapacious hungers, unstable disappointments.

Making her way down side streets to Piazza di San Lorenzo, Ora ducked into Café Vitti, drank down an iced Campari and soda before crossing the piazza, a glaring triangular hell at this hour, and took refuge in the fifth-century church of San Lorenzo in Lucina. She went down a row of side chapels, clattering euros into slotted metal boxes, buying minute illuminations of paintings—portraits of martyrs and saints, apocryphal scenes of conversion, assumption, crucifixion, ascension, resurrection. On view beneath one marble altar was a preserved section of the gridiron San Lorenzo, St. Laurence, had been roasted alive on. Beneath another, the wax-colored skull of Pope St. Alexander. Under the main altar lay the body of St. Pontian with three nameless companions. Ora wavered, slightly drunk, among the bones and dust of these saintly and otherwise departed. On her way out, she stopped before a candelabra of electric candles, switched on a single, weak, amber filament for Giles.

Ora remembered to keep a few coins in her pocket to place in the outstretched, unwashed hands and plastic cups of Rome's beggars, a "travel tip" in her guide book. Emerging from San Lorenzo, she nearly fell over the prostrate figure of a woman shrouded in black rags, begging beside one of the portico's Ionic columns. Startled, Ora rained her day's coins, all of them, into the empty cup between the woman's filthy, swollen hands. They made a jackpot noise, yet the figure remained still, rough sun beating down on the lump of black, bulky rags. What if she was dead? Surely it happened. Ora bent close, wondering who she should go to for help. But at her touch, the figure stirred, moaned, and the awl-sharp bone she felt beneath the black cloth seemed as horrifying to Ora as death. She moved away.

Passing exclusive shops, their open doors exhaling scented, cooled air, Ora succumbed and went into a leather shop on Via Fratelli. She purchased a wallet she didn't need, salmon pink with navy silk lining and a blue leather tassel. On Via Borgognona, a side street near the Spanish Steps, she found Restaurante Nino, the place Giles had been eager to try. Inside, above a high wainscoting of dark polished wood, cream-colored walls were hung with black-and-white photographs, portraits of Rome in the 1930s. Polleny light from overhead lamps burnished dark wood tables set with immaculate white linen. Male waiters in black pants, black bow ties, and white jackets with wide, starched lapels stood at appointed stations, white linen cloths draped over their arms, paper pads and pencils in their jacket pockets. Against one wall of the dining room was a curious wood pulpit. Perched inside like a parakeet, presiding between a black rotary phone and a fat reservation book, sat a tiny woman in a crepe de chine dress of pink, green, and black print, her clipped, tawny hair brushed forward in a dry, avian frill or ruff.

The headwaiter formally seated Ora at the last open spot, a table for five. Within minutes, a British family—father, mother, and girl of perhaps ten, wearing an old-fashioned straw hat with a black grosgrain ribbon—was seated at the table with her. The father acknowledged Ora with a polite, dissolving smile, the wife and daughter looked through her as if she were a lesser ghost of Rome. Drinks were ordered, the girl's a lemonade, her parents' a bottle of Cabernet, while the man (Ora called him Nigel) pressed across the table toward his sere, nut-brown wife, describing his tour of some necropolis or other, spewing enthusiasms like fertilizer pellets—everything "spectacular," "astonishing," "damned incredible," "utterly fantastic." He flung facts with equal verve—Constantine, St. Peter, Nero, the Etruscans, the Romans, a recently verified Christian code—as his wife, with grim, swift practice, drained glass after glass of wine.

Ora eavesdropped, her indictments fleeting, unserious. She shamelessly loathed the vinegar-faced wife, admired the child studying her bright red menu before whispering to her father, "Daddy, there are *brains* on this menu." "Really?" asked Nigel. "Where?" "Underneath the fried foods." Nodding affably, Nigel carried on, talking of tombs, countless tombs he had seen, entire families entombed. Who, the child asked, was the youngest person in the tombs? Without the least condescension, he answered, "A fourteen-year-old girl, darling, hardly older than you." So the child was included, her age-appropriate interests—brains and tombs—acknowledged but not catered to. Exactly how Ora and Giles would have raised a child had they been able to have one—the one wish denied them. Self-possessed beneath her wide-brimmed straw hat, the child (a Sophie or an Evie) easily navigated between her parents' grown-up, surface talk and her own green and hidden, burgeoning world.

"Awesome!" Nigel barked, after a first bite of cannelloni di Nino, the house dish. According to Giles, the Tuscan menu, scarcely changed since the restaurant's opening in 1930, served traditional dishes, *ribollita, pappardelle, vitello tonnato.* Nigel's dour wife (a Maud, a Mabel) shrugged. Clearly, his enthusiasms were ecumenical, not confined to sightseeing, so Ora was forced to reconsider, from Maud/Mabel's perspective, how such indiscriminate gushing over everyone and everything might prove, over a marriage of long duration, even one year, tiresome. Giles used to insist there was a chronic wound in any marital dynamic, one terminal irritant, though he and Ora proved happily exempt. Giles had been a chef, inventive, sensual, and wildly fond of food (his corpulence, his passion for butter and cheese, steak and morels, had killed him) and throughout their marriage, Ora had loved him, though perhaps not sufficiently. One never loved anyone enough, not while they were alive. After death, myth took over. Sentimentality. She paid her bill as Nigel enthused about his upcoming trip to Madagascar, oblivious to his wife's rosacea-blotched, acid face.

Back at the Majestic, her room had received its turn-down service, white hotel slippers set out on a white mat, fresh sheets and pristine duvet folded back so she could slip into the bed's chilled, narrow envelope. It was not yet nine o'clock, but Ora fell into an exhausted sleep, her feet burning, as if on fire, martyred, from the heat and hours of walking.

III

At sunrise, she flung open the shutters, the window. The orange bowler car, the stranger in his summer blue shirt, still there—like loyalty.

Stretching both large, speckled eggshell arms above her head, Ora Fitz unpinned and shook down her heavy brown hair. Her nipples, round and pink as the Joséphine de Beauharnais roses Giles had cultivated with such pleasure, tightened in the cool air as she bent down to step into a pair of black silk panties, then turned toward the open window to fasten her black lace bra, leaning forward to better display her scented, magnificent breasts. A heavy-set, reticent woman, increasingly uncertain of herself as she aged, Ora Fitz had spent two years mourning Giles, two years contracting into invisibility, shrinking to inconsequence. Yet in this neat space of a window, with a man staring up at her—she felt his eyes on her now—she became Aphrodite, aroused, lush, dangerous. With studied care, she buttoned her Swiss-dotted blouse, twisted and fastened her hair with a tortoiseshell clasp, looked to him for acknowledgement, saw none. The sensations, tremulous, were of fierce duration.

Breakfast on the garden terrace—black iron chairs and tables, white linens in a transept pattern across the gray marble tabletops, sand-colored umbrellas. A waiter spritzed pigeons with water from a plastic spray bottle. The birds fluttered off, circled, returned. Several Italian families were up early, the fathers handsome in linen shorts and polo shirts the colors of the sea—azure, faded marine—the colors of summer—ochre, tangerine, lemon. Ora traced and retraced the coolness of the water glass beneath her fingertips, wrote half-observations in her small red journal. She had begun doing this to appear less lonely and because she hoped writing a thing down delayed its erasure. Suddenly, she set her pen down, shocked by a thought, an idea that made perfect sense.

The Majestic Hotel was staffed by men in gray uniforms with maroon striping, by waiters in black and white. Plain, middle-aged men past their prime, courteous and discreet. One man opened the entrance door for her each morning as she left the hotel, another stepped onto Via Veneto to flag a taxi for her, another rolled a cart of folded, laundered towels and fragrant soaps past her in the hallway. Her breakfast waiter, Sandro, took her order with amiable subservience. Another, on her first night, delivered room service. Winter red currants, dusky grapes, pale wedges of brie and havarti, a chilled glass of Chardonnay, all set elegantly on a white clothed table, with Ora, acutely aware of her nakedness beneath the hotel's thin white robe so that it seemed an act of intimacy, signing the bill he held out, borrowing his black-and-gold pen.

He could park his car on the side street outside the hotel, do his day's work and be gone by evening. She might have spoken with him, more than once. If he worked at the hotel, it would hardly be difficult for him to locate her room, number 203.

The possibility that she had been exposing herself to a man she knew even slightly, unbalanced her. When Sandro brought a second cup of cappuccino, *special for madame*, a beige heart shape in its foam, her face went hot. When she tried to slip away without his noticing, he cheerfully called out, *Arrivederla, Madame*. And when the tall, uniformed man in the lobby swung the front door wide, saying with accented graciousness, *Have a nice day, Madame Fitz,* Ora could only nod, her expression false, absurdly demure.

Walking down shaded gravel paths through the ancient Villa Borghese gardens, she arrived early at the Galleria Borghese and stood waiting among a knot of other tourists for her prebooked tour time. Once inside, she found her audio guide was broken, the descriptions unmatched to any of the paintings or sculptures. For several minutes, she tried coordinating the guide with her location, then gave up and simply wandered the gilt maze of rooms. When she came upon Bernini's sculpture, the Rape of Persephone, she was transfixed by the god of the underworld's fingers digging into, dimpling the marble flesh of the girl's thigh and waist, oddly excited and disturbed by this exquisite depiction of imminent sexual violence, violation. In the next room, she sank down on the room's only chair, conquered by the sublime terror of Bernini's Apollo and Daphne. A young virgin, Daphne, escaping her pursuer by transforming herself into a laurel tree, her slender fingertips turning to delicate translucent leaves, white tendrils of roots snaking from her sandals, her chaste, perfect limbs covered in rough bark.

So many unpleasant, difficult things had happened to Ora, disappointments, betrayals, illnesses, infertility, unexpected deaths. She had gradually withdrawn, tightened the circumference of her actions. If she appeared to live, it was fugitive life. She had turned, not into a laurel tree, but to stone.

Back at the hotel, Ora dined at so early an hour, five o'clock, she was alone in the enormous, chilly room with its great urns of white star lilies, blue delphinium, and pink roses, its oversize mirrors and glittering chandeliers. When a father with three adolescent boys was given a table behind her, their combined silence went on so long Ora, curious, glanced back. All four, the father, too, slumped down in their chairs scrolling, texting, scanning messages on their cell phones. Strange. She and Giles had never run out of things to say, had played and laughed late into most nights. When they were alone, they behaved like children.

Up until the moment his overtaxed heart had burst, his consciousness fading out in front of her—breath gone before the ambulance arrived— Giles had worshipped Ora's wide-hipped, generous body, adored her very existence. He was a rare man, the only man she knew who saw no demarcation, no distinction between flesh and spirit. He had given her the gift of a deeply private, uninhibited erotic life. Unmoored, she came to Rome, tracing steps they had never taken.

IV

Languid, she caressed, squeezed, one rose-colored nipple. With her other hand, she felt how wet she was, and with him looking up at her, watching, she brought herself to orgasm, the first since Giles' death. *Lewd,* her mother's derision, *disgusting,* her students' revulsion, *shameless puss, old cunt,* the world's recoil and punishment. Ora shuddered, her face contorting.

She might have worried she was going mad, might have been appalled, frightened. But this was the old, playful hunger, hers and Giles', reenacted in the space of a window. Ora considered, not for the first time, how society rushed forward, day after day in its observable order, an order held together by unfathomable sexual secrets.

On the terrace later that morning, Ora watched her waiter attend to another table of hotel guests and found herself aching for his slight, courteous figure, thinning hair, the weary set of his shoulders. She wondered what it would be like, if he came to her.

Sex, she wrote in her red book, survives grief...desire outlasts loyalty.

The walk to the Etruscan museum was longer than it had appeared on her map. She had badly underestimated the distance. Laboring uphill through the Villa Borghese gardens, following infrequent signs, she kept to the shade of trees until there were no trees, only sun. She asked two policemen parked in a blue police car for directions; they pointed past the gardens, up another long, steep hill. She began to worry about heatstroke—she had brought no water, forgotten her umbrella, no one was around. When she came to a large oyster-colored building that turned out to be the Museum of Modern Art, she walked around one side of the building until she found its café, a stark, white space with life-size sculptures of nudes, black and abstract. She ordered a cold drink, pink, bitter, strong. It arrived with small dishes of nuts, olives, and potato chips. There, her lunch. A fastidious-looking man sat nearby, eating nothing, reading a newspaper. Besides her, he was the only customer in the café.

When her waiter insisted the Etruscan museum was far, much too far to walk, Ora thought to call a taxi, but the cashier disagreed and said no, no, it's a short walk, five minutes. Muzzy from drink and the afternoon heat, she left the café and trudged on. Only a tourist, she thought, would be walking up an unshaded hill at two o'clock, the temperature over one hundred degrees. But the cashier had been right; within minutes, she found Villa Giulia. Grateful to be out of the heat, Ora stood before glassed-in exhibits of Etruscan burial artifacts, dutifully reading printed descriptions. But the immaculate, quiet rooms, empty of visitors, made her feel drugged, heavy-limbed, half asleep. Abandoning any pretense of finding these rooms of Etruscan detritus fascinating, Ora saw a spiral staircase and descended the plain, white steps until she stood before a pre-Roman tomb excavated from a site in northern Lazio, brought to Villa Giulia, and meticulously reconstructed.

It's so much cooler down here. Almost cold. The rock walls of the tomb were lively with chipped, fading, frescoes. Gray dolphins, eternally exuberant, arched up from cobalt waves, athletes with spears balanced naked on the broad, muscular backs of red-spotted horses, couples reclined at banquet tables, feeding delicacies, with lasting tenderness, into one another's mouths. A pugilist boxed, fists striking nothing.

Ora stepped over the low cordoning rope, lay down on ochre burial soil. Underground air sealed itself around her, and crossing her arms over her chest, she wept.

A decent woman, a widow, should draw a veil over her used body. A decent woman should know when to close up shop, descend the staircase, shorn of longing. A woman as fortunate in love as Ora had been, even that woman, should descend, without further animal embrace, into the crypt marked with her name.

*

In bed, the place they felt free, almost immortal, Giles loved to tease her, inventing carnal games, calling sex his "night medicine," and Ora his fat-fannied, rosy-nippled pigeon, his naughty, naughty nurse. Until she really was.

She told no one, kept secret to her death the one dangerous thing, the resurrecting act, revolting to the world if it ever knew, she invited in. On her last night in Rome, Ora left her hotel door unlocked and went to sleep, her body impenitent, spirit wanting.

Before sunrise, the door opened. She sensed his closeness, a conspiracy, the shedding of shoes, belt, pants, shirt. In darkness, she touched her fingers to his face, imagined she knew him. As he loosened her limbs from the white-sheeted, narrow plinth of bed, she thought to tell him her night's strange dream, sucking the ugly, swollen cock of some faceless, grotesque monster. Instead she took his cock—surprising, hot smelling, familiar—into her artful, swimming mouth, urged him with her great sun flowering hunger, urged him on until they both cried lost, found–*Marco!*–*Polo!*–children in thrall to, gaming at, love.

Near the bed, his shirt, eternal blue of summer.

WEIKE WANG
Conversations with My Father

He said the sky is not blue or white or gray. It is the color of one septillion snowflakes falling to the ground. He said a septillion is one followed by twenty-four zeros. More zeros than you could ever write down in one sitting because you are an impatient child. An only child. A singularity, as he would call me when he did not feel like saying my full name.

He said things like how many corners does a table have if you cut one off? I said three, but the answer was five. How stupid of me. And he said this too, how stupid of you to say a number like three. Three rhymes with trees, I said. And he shook his head. Three is for the triangle, he said, which is the most stable shape you will ever know. And what comes after three? Well, there's four and five and six, I said. And then? And then I didn't know. I guessed infinity and he shook his head again. How stupid of you, he said, infinity is not a number; it's a direction, like an arrow that never ends. He said, count things in your free time so that you will never forget the sequence of more things to come. Pens were things. Books were things. How many things? he asked me. And I held up two, five, six fingers, meaning two hundred fifty-six things I had just counted on my way home from pre k. And what is two hundred fifty-six cut in half and chopped to quarters and taken to the nth power? Nth? I asked. Meaning limit, this is a limit problem, don't you understand?

He said on my birthday, you are now four thousand fifteen days old. He said, and on this birthday, you can have the natural log of that in balloons. And if you can't figure out what I mean, then you can't have balloons at all. He said at the dinner table, chew with periodicity or just swallow it whole. He said in the mornings, pour me zero point six-six cubic deciliters of 1 percent milk.

He said, multiply, divide, add, and then subtract, in that order because that is the order of operations and the way anything gets done. He said, sit down, be quiet, and let me show you how to do math. Here is a square root, a rational root, a rational root with a square root, a reciprocal, a conjugate, a complex conjugate that is a pain to solve.

He said, here is an imaginary answer that does not exist until I write down the letter i and then it does, right there on the page. He said, pay attention because you're not paying attention, you're drifting. And he was right, I wasn't paying attention. I was drifting.

He said, if you learned math as fast as you read books, then you might be a genius, but you're not a genius, you're a hole where knowledge goes to sleep. He said, play with your dolls for no more than half an hour, no more than fifteen minutes, no more than a second, a millisecond, actually just put those dolls down and come here and let me show you how to do math. Here is a formula, another formula, a quadratic formula that you must memorize and know as well as you know the national anthem of this country that is not my country because your mother and I are immigrants, but you, you are not, so put down those dolls and watch me do math. He said, here is a theorem. Here is another theorem. And here is the simplest of all theorems that has never been proven, unless you are a genius, which you are not. He said, come here, my singularity, and let me show you how to do math. And I said yes one thousand four hundred seventy times until I said no, I hate math. I can't stand it. And he said, quite calmly, you are no child of mine.

He said on a mountaintop, I feel the pressure differential in my veins. He said on an elevator, this is normal force at its best. He said at a movie theater, I can't understand anything, they're talking too fast. He said at a restaurant, this is not what I ordered. This has cheese in it. Take it back. He said in the evenings, tell me the time. No, not like that. Tell me the time in arcseconds per second or don't tell me at all.

He said, sit down, be quiet, and let me show how to do physics. Without physics, you will be ignorant of the world. You will be empty, hollow, and unable to articulate why, for instance, a rocket flies through the void your teachers call outer space. And why does a rocket fly in space? he asked. I said I didn't know. I didn't even guess. How stupid of me. And he said this too, how stupid of you to not even guess. Here is why a rocket flies through space, and you must remember because I'm not saying it again. He said, wire your old dollhouse and then you will understand electricity. He said, wire this bathroom light and then you will really understand electricity. Put the galvanometer here and here and don't shock yourself. See what happens when you don't listen to me? You've shocked yourself. Now stand up and try it again. Again.

Again. Again. He said, when you push on a wall, the wall pushes back on you. And for this reason, rockets fly through outer space. He said, listen for the Doppler effect or you will never understand sound, and if you never understand sound, then you will never understand melody or harmony or the reason a violin is shaped the way that it is. He said, come here, my singularity, and let me show you how real projectiles fly. He said, here is a stone that you must skip eleven times, no more, no less, you have to get your launch angle just right. I threw the stone down. I said I wasn't skipping anything. I was going two thousand nine hundred seventy miles away. And he said quite calmly, you are definitely no child of mine.

But still, he said things like do your taxes early. Pay your bills on time. And don't tip like a moron. Do the 18 percent in your head. He said, don't cheap out on your insurance. Think about your 401k. Think about a high-interest savings account or don't do either and be poor for the rest of your life. Think about the children that you currently do not have, because if they're anything like you, they'll want things that you truly do not have. He said, come here, my singularity, and let me show you how to plan. But I didn't come. I stayed where I was, which was still two thousand nine hundred seventy miles away. And for a while we did not speak.

Until we did, thirty-seven point two years later when he and I were both already old. He said, you have on exactly sixty-five fine pearls. And to my husband, he said, you are very white and also a hundred ninety-six centimeters tall.

LUCY BIEDERMAN
Border Songs: A Look2 Essay on Américo Paredes

Deep, deep down in the southernmost part of South Texas sits the city of Brownsville. The landscape is home to countless ranches, endless dry brush, and thousands of recent migrants to the US from Mexico. Brownsville is seventy miles south of where the US Border Patrol operates one of its busiest traffic checkpoints, in Falfurrias, Texas. According to an article in *The New York Times* late last year, this checkpoint "apprehends the largest number of people that have entered the country illegally—14,243 from October 2014 to August [2015]." South Texas is a place where the Border looms everywhere: revered and reviled, and often transgressed. And Brownsville, flush against it, is the birthplace of Américo Paredes, a multilingual folklorist whose writing records the sounds, sights, and textures of life on the Texas-Mexico border.

Paredes, writes the literary scholar and cultural theorist José Limón, is "the leading Mexican-American scholar/intellectual/creative writer of our time." All those slashes are telling—and they might be why you haven't heard of him. (And why Limón has: the noted academic was a student of Paredes and wrote a genre-transgressing masterpiece, *Dancing with the Devil*, in 1994.) It is possible that the very disciplinary and generic boundaries that Paredes exploded in his writing are responsible for his lack of notoriety. Paredes worked in a wide variety of forms, from lyric poetry to academic scholarship. His hybrid-genre books are interspersed among more traditionally conceived scholarship, making it easy to consider him, particularly from a distance, a capital-S scholar, not a public intellectual, not a journalist, nor a musician, novelist, or poet—despite his having been all that and more. He died in 1999, but many of his best books mix genre and form in innovative ways that presage some of the twenty-first century's most renowned experimental writers.

Even before receiving his bachelor's degree at the nontraditional age of thirty-five, Paredes was writing and publishing in both English and Spanish. His multiple volumes of poetry began with *Cantos de adolescencia* (1937), published in Mexico when he was twenty-two. Paredes wrote much of his fiction and poetry before returning to school, resulting in an early body of work that did not see publication until decades after it was written, once he had established a formidable reputation as a scholar of Mexican American folkways. During his first year as a professor, Paredes tossed off a novel just for a shot at a $500 prize being offered. He won it. The novel *George Washington Gómez* (1990), which Paredes wrote between 1935 and 1940 and then stashed in a drawer for 50 years, the scholar Shelley Fisher Fishkin now calls among "the most important works in twentieth-century American literature."

There isn't a typical Américo Paredes book, genre, or style. *With His Pistol in His Hand: A Border Ballad and Its Hero* (1958), Paredes' best-known book, exemplifies his extraordinary range as a scholar/ intellectual/creative writer, to use Limón's formulation. The book fuses academic balladry scholarship, lyric storytelling, cultural ethnography, and journalistic recovery work—all by looking closely at a single folksong, "The Ballad of Gregorio Cortez." Some of Paredes' other important academic folklore books include *Toward New Perspectives in Folklore* (1972, with Richard Bauman), *A Texas-Mexican Cancionero: Folksongs of the Lower Border* (1976), *Folklore and Culture on the Texas-Mexican Border* (1993), and dozens of academic studies of Mexican, American, and Mexican American folklore, written in both Spanish and English. In essays like "The Folk Base of Chicano Literature" (1979) and "The Problem of Identity in a Changing Culture" (1993), Paredes uses his interdisciplinary perspective to assert beyond doubt that, as Audre Lorde says, poetry is not a luxury. Looking at daily life, folklore, and literature, Paredes cannot help but see the vital links between them that most of us miss entirely.

Within all his literary variety, Paredes wasn't so much an experimentalist as a pragmatist. He *had* to write, so he wrote, genre be damned. He wasn't trying to find his voice or his story; he already had his story. Born in 1915, Paredes grew up on the Texas side of the Texas-Mexico border, where the distinctions between the two cultures and their languages were sometimes indiscernible, and sometimes as loud as a rifle blast. In the Paredeses' Spanish-speaking household, Mexican traditions prevailed; meanwhile, at the mostly white public schools Paredes attended, lessons were in English and often conveyed cruel stereotypes about Mexican Americans. By the time he enrolled in the doctoral program at Austin, he was already pushing forty. He was no gull fresh out of undergrad hoping to hop on the tenure-line gravy train. To attend graduate school, he had left a successful journalistic career that included covering war crimes trials in Tokyo and working as a PR man for the Red Cross. He had fought as an infantryman in World War II. Through it all, he encountered racism of many varieties—paid lower wages for the same work, overlooked by educators, passed over for promotions. When he entered academe's old boy network in the early 1950s, he had long been awake to truths that even most of his professors were not ready to acknowledge.

The Texas-Mexico border that Paredes spent his life writing about, from his youth through his years as an emeritus professor, was both under- and over-imagined. It was a site of mythic battles between good guys and bad guys. It was also a site of a people, Americans of Mexican heritage, that went unrecognized in the country in which they putatively belonged. The awkward subtitle of *George Washington Gómez: A Mexicotexan Novel* speaks to the situation Paredes was dealing with. He wrote before words like Chicano/a, Latina/o, and Hispanic had cultural or academic currency. As he wrote, he summoned his experience and that of his "folk" into the official culture. The coming-of-age of Paredes' George Washington Gómez, or Guálinto, as he is known by everyone, is mediated at every turn by issues of culture, community, and belonging.

George Washington Gómez is the story of Guálinto's childhood and young adulthood in the lower-class barrio of Jonesville-on-the-Grande, a substitution for the Brownsville of Paredes' youth. (Jonesville-on-the-Grande is also the setting of many of the short stories in Paredes' *The Hammon and the Bean*.) Paredes sets Guálinto's story in a broader context, including the failed uprising by South Texan *sediciosos* in 1915, the Great Depression (known in the book as *La Chilla*), segregation, and World War II. As Guálinto comes into self-consciousness, suffers and recovers from a serious illness, enters school, endures bullying, makes friends, finds and loses love, and works his first job, he is affected, often deeply, by the turbulence of the economic and social landscape that mark the early twentieth century.

Some of the most formally compelling passages in *George Washington Gómez* are about *La Chilla*. Departing from Guálinto's story, Paredes zooms out for a long chapter, providing pointed, but often lyrical, social critique. The Depression took its time getting to the Rio Grande Valley, particularly to its poorest residents, Mexican American farmworkers. A typical Border laborer, Paredes writes,

> could not imagine a state of things where he would be poorer than he already was. He heard about the people of Oklahoma, who were leaving their land, getting on their trucks and going west. To the Mexicotexan laborer, anybody who owned a truck was rich. He heard of some sharecropper families who had nothing to eat but flour and bacon. The Mexican laborer, who had subsisted on tortillas most of his life, wondered how people who could afford biscuits and bacon could be poor.

There is cutting social critique throughout the rest of the novel, as well. For example, driving home after being turned away from a high-school event at a Mexican-themed club that, it turns out, has a no-Mexicans policy, one of Guálinto's classmates tells a story: "When I was in fifth grade I wrote a theme once, in geography class. About the population of Texas. And I said, 'Texas is a very big state with very little people.' The teacher took off five points for that. She said it was bad diction."

Like the greatest, longest novels of Naturalist literature—Wharton's *The Custom of the Country* (1913), Dreiser's *An American Tragedy* (1925)— *George Washington Gómez* describes the disappointing stringency of society's expectations. Guálinto has some of the charisma of Mark Twain's Huck Finn, and is, like Richard Wright's Bigger Thomas in *Native Son*, formed to a great extent by his social conditions. But Guálinto resists the hero status that often attaches to literary characters when we read them for the first time. As a little boy, told by his mother and uncle that he is special, better, destined to be a leader of his people, Guálinto rallies. "Just wait till I'm a man! I'll get our land back. I'll be like Gregorio Cortez," he tells his uncle. Cortez, the hero of the *corrido* (ballad) that Paredes writes about in *With His Pistol in His Hand*, looms over Guálinto as a model for Mexican American manhood. By his teenage years, though, Guálinto seethes against that prescription. Guálinto knows what his family, and his more optimistic friends, takes much longer to grasp: He just isn't that great a guy. He is smart but not clever; he is petty, selfish, spoiled; in other words, Guálinto is a man, not a hero. The cultural critic William Nericcio has designated the "fertile, intoxicating terrain of Américo Paredes [as] the domain of ethnic American self-loathing." As an "ethnic American," why should Guálinto be denied the self-loathing that invades our native arts, buttresses the defensive sounds of our favorite sitcoms?

As Guálinto sinks into despair, threatening to drop out of high school during a family crisis, his (red-haired) friend El Colorado tries to inspire him. El Colorado talks for pages—he seems to have long held his story inside.

> "What if my father don't know how to read? I know how, don't I? What if my mother don't even know what an accountant is? I know what an accountant is, and I want to be one. And I'm going to be one, whatever it costs me. I'll show these bastards!" He stopped, exhausted and hoarse from the longest speech he had ever made to anyone in his life, and he looked at Guálinto with a timid expression on his big, freckle-splotched face as if the baring of these inner thoughts of his had somehow made him vulnerable. Guálinto looked at him admiringly. The red-head was a better man than himself. "He could really have done something great," he thought. "He's the kind of guy I should have been." He tried to say it but the words stuck in his throat. Instead he said, "You're a fighter, I'm a coward."

Guálinto takes a few cracks at love throughout the novel. He tries, in this passage, to love his good friend as El Colorado deserves to be loved. But Guálinto doesn't seem to have it in him. Although Guálinto has renounced the corridos of his childhood, they cast their shadows over him: In his self-pity, he sees a world of only good vs. evil, fighters vs. cowards. In the space between fighter and coward, of course, is where real life takes place.

In his studies of folklore, Paredes shows how Guálinto might have developed such a mindset. Paredes analyzes how everything from corridos to jokes shapes one's experience of the world. He seeks fact with a journalist's rigor, then interrogates his findings with a poststructuralist's cynicism.

This is particularly true in *With His Pistol in His Hand*. Paredes submitted *With His Pistol in His Hand* as his doctoral thesis in 1954, and the University of Texas-Austin Press published it as a book four years later. The book centers on Paredes' study of "The Ballad of Gregorio

Cortez," a popular corrido in Mexican ranching communities in the Rio Grande Valley. The ballad is of unknown authorship, but Paredes traces its first performances to the summer of 1901, weeks after the real-life Gregorio Cortez Lira shot and killed a Texas sheriff in self-defense and, for several days, outran and outwitted hundreds of racist, bloodthirsty Texas Rangers before finally surrendering, under renegotiated and more humane terms. As a common variant of the ballad ends,

> Then said Gregorio Cortez,
> With his pistol in his hand,
> "Ah, so many mounted Rangers
> Just to take one Mexican!"

With His Pistol in His Hand is a book as hybrid as the culture it describes. The book is divided into two parts, its first something of an ethnography—a cultural and historical introduction to border life, as if to say, you cannot begin to understand "The Ballad of Gregorio Cortez" without knowing the people who sing it. In the book's "Part One," Paredes combines the twice-told and the never-mentioned, devoting a chapter to Cortez the legend, and a chapter to Cortez the man, using court records, letters, and interviews to reconstruct a history that most official sources had done their best to erase or control.

Even the materials Paredes worked from testify to the racist, Anglo-centric history and practices of Border life. The sources he cites include newspaper reports that refer to Cortez as the "arch fiend." Much of the history of the Border he pieces together relies not on published accounts, but on other University of Texas students' master's theses, for the simple reason that there were no published accounts from which to draw. The folklore scholar Marilyn Motz has defined folklore as "fugitive knowledge." *With His Pistol in His Hand* demonstrates how knowledge becomes fugitive, and not just because Cortez is a literal fugitive, on a flight from the law in life and legend. Michel Foucault famously characterized our age as one in which the truth itself matters less than does the status of the truth. *With His Pistol in His Hand* is a book about how struggles over the status of truth affect real peoples' lives. If the things you know are considered "fugitive" rather than "official," what does that suggest about who you are?

Before Cortez was memorialized as lore, he was a person, just like anybody else, eating meals and resting with his wife on the porch. On June 12, 1901, the day that Cortez ended up leaving his house forever, Paredes writes,

> He had just finished the noon meal and was lying full length on the floor of the front gallery of his house…, his head on his wife's lap. Sitting outside with them were his mother, his brother Romaldo, and Romaldo's wife. The children were inside, still eating. It was hot and clear; the corn was tall and promised a good harvest. There was cause to be contented. It was at that moment that Sheriff Morris appeared looking for horse thieves.

"There is much variation in oral accounts concerning Cortez's personal appearance," Paredes reports, sifting through the descriptions he has collected from people for whom Gregorio Cortez is a household name. Paredes notes that "as the story moves farther away from fact into legend, the narrator identifies himself personally with Cortez." As the legend of Cortez circulated, the often-ignored people living on this often-ignored Border took the opportunity to tell their own stories—to place their lives within legend. "A short, very dark man told me that Cortez had been just a little dark man, *chiquitito y prietito.* Ah, but what a man!" Paredes writes; meanwhile, "The variant according to which Gregorio is a field hand was given to me by laboring people." Paredes' goal in the first section of *With His Pistol In His Hand* seems not so much to record lore, or even to bring to light the facts behind the legend. Instead, in the many glimpses it offers of Mexican American life at a certain time and place—from lying peacefully on the front porch at noon to the importance of masculinity and manhood—this unclassifiable book hints at the vistas of peoples that have fallen from the official record. And of all those who were never on the record in the first place. Paredes shows that Cortez's story was circulated, and ascended into lore, even as it was unfolding. The alacrity with which that transformation took place suggests how "fugitive" or "unofficial" peoples construct the sense of cultural significance that mainstream culture withholds from them.

The second section of the book is about the song itself, "The Ballad of Gregorio Cortez," with a history of the Border corrido form, variants of the ballad in English and Spanish, and line-for-line analyses. Paredes pinpoints the original time and place of each variant based on how and when performers would have received the information within its stanzas.

Paredes' books are replete with images of father figures passing down lore. His dedication to *With His Pistol in His Hand* appears in the form of a poem:

> To the memory of my father
> who rode a raid or two with
> Catarino Garza;
> and to all those old men
> who sat around on summer nights,
> in the days when there was
> a chaparral, smoking their
> cornhusk cigarettes and talking
> in low, gentle voices about
> violent things;
> while I listened.

As Limón points out, the poetic form of these words signals that "this is no conventional dedication, and what follows is no conventional book." Paredes' practice of writing lyric poems as dedications to academic books is an initiation into his expansive way of thinking about discipline and genre. Here, a lyric statement about oral storytelling frames an academic study.

Paredes is a foundational figure in a tradition of books that combine literary and critical theory, fiction, poetry, memoir, and folklore to express hybrid cultural and ethnic identities. Although Paredes is not a familiar name among creative writers, his stylistic and intellectual influence runs deep. Writing in and against Paredes' example, Gloria Anzaldúa, author of the work of critical theory/poetry/memoir *Borderlands*/La Frontera: *The New Mestiza*, kickstarted a Chicana feminist movement that has included Ana Castillo, Sandra Cisneros, and Julia Alvarez. These writers, like Paredes, are fluent in multiple languages and genres, and tend to combine them in unexpected ways. Paredes variously influenced and prefigured what scholar Christopher Douglas calls the "literary multiculturalism" of contemporary masters like Toni Morrison, N. Scott Momaday, and Ishmael Reed.

Paredes makes mincemeat, throughout his work, of the long tradition of white writers, like J. Frank Dobie and Walter Prescott Webb, who wrote romanticized histories of Texas that cast the Texas Rangers in the role of courageous good guys. The studies of Mexican American communities that they claimed to have put painstaking effort into, Paredes exposes as mere racialized misunderstandings, assumptions, and guesses. In other words, fiction. Further, historians and folklorists like Dobie and Webb promoted their own reputations and fame by exploiting the racist expectations of their general and academic audiences. In *Dancing With the Devil*, Limón shares the awful factoid that Dobie encouraged people to call him Pancho, a cartoonish appropriation of the culture and language he purported to translate. In *George Washington Gómez*, Paredes lampoons Dobie in the character of K. Hank Harvey, "a local luminary" who gives a high-school graduation speech to an auditorium of politely unamused Jonesville residents. Harvey, the perfect inverse of Paredes, has a readymade audience and nothing to say.

Paredes' expansive work, crossing disciplines and genres, suggests *surplus*—too much to say, having waited too long to say it. In *George Washington Gómez*, peoples' stories, although they have never told them to anyone before, come bursting out of them, overlong and fully formed, like the adult-shaped babies in Renaissance paintings. Toward the end of the novel, Juan, the stolid farmhand of George's uncle Feliciano, reveals to Guálinto with surprising eagerness some key information. "Juan talked for a long time, longer than he had talked to anyone in years. When he finished he sighed and said, 'I have been wanting to tell you all this for months now. I'm glad I did.'" One gets the sense that nearly all the characters in the novel, from George's slightly unhinged mother, Maria, to his pretentious former schoolmate Francisco, are itching for the space and audience to tell their personal histories, having been unheard most of their lives. Like Paredes, they have their stories. They merely lack an audience.

This urgency may be inevitable when one lives in the type of place that the scholar Mary Louise Pratt has termed a "contact zone," a place where a "we" meets a "them." Paredes laments in *With His Pistol in*

His Hand that border ballads have hardly been studied at all, "having received to date but passing attention from the Texas folklorist and almost none at all from the Mexican ballad student." If it's not one or the other, easy to file as Southern or Western or Texan or Mexican or American, theory or history, we tend to turn away. But it's never one or the other. Paredes' writing may be the best example of the hybrid songs we sing in America, even when we don't know we're singing them.

*Book Recommendations from
Our Advisory Editors*

Ann Beattie recommends *Forty Martyrs* by Philip F. Deaver: "These are grown-up stories about grown-ups. Subtly linked and beautifully written, their subject is loss (and possible redemption), played against a backdrop of Everywhere, America, that, in his hands, isn't."

Robert Boswell recommends *Calle Florista* by Connie Voisine: "This is a remarkable book by one of our best poets, one of those rare books that is unflinching in its honesty and yet makes the reader grateful to be part of the show."

Jane Hirshfield recommends *Works On Paper* by Jennifer Barber: "winner of The Word Works' 2015 Tenth Gate Prize is a book of etched clarities and deftly subtle deepenings. Virtually every page is weighted with the resonance and harmonics of meaning that can only be found by way of poetry's particular seeing. Barber is a poet of acute perception, sensibility, range, and gesture. She draws her statements equally from the detailed, discernable known and from a sane acknowledgment of our ultimate unknowing. These poems of our interconnected lives, loves, questions, and losses are vessels carrying sustenance palpably needed—as water, yeast, honey, and flour are needed, and kneaded, for bread."

Tony Hoagland recommends *Finestra's Window* by Patricia Corbus: "This poet you've never heard of is superb, figuratively and rhetorically adroit; she has the streamlined playfulness of her poetic lineage, Wallace Stevens and Mary Ruefle, and like them she has poignant depths, and existential gravitas." Also, Hoagland is reading and already rereading Vivian Gornick's *The Odd Woman and the City*: "Gornick simply can't be praised enough; her genius for psychological directness, her penetrating meditations on her life and what literature means to the making of culture and humanity—her sensibility itself testifies to the joy and worth of the examined life."

Maura Stanton recommends *Can I Finish, Please?* by Catherine Bowman: "This marvelous book is full of passion and obsession. Everything sticks to a walking stick, the ghost of a big blue wolf dog goes Ahroooooo, and James Schuyler shows up on the ferry pulling out of Boston Harbor."

Gerald Stern recommends the immediate rereading of Howard Zinn's *A People's History of the United States* as a background reader for current elections.

Rosanna Warren recommends *The Fate of Ideas* by Robert Boyers: "To read Robert Boyers is to take a walk with an ebulliently talkative, erudite, and unpredictable companion. Veering from gossip to aphorism to analysis, Boyers muses about integrity, beauty, fidelity, art, politics, and friendship. We are invited to think alongside Susan Sontag, Karl Kraus, Lionel Trilling, Zadie Smith, Adam Zagajewski, Clement Greenberg, Frank Kermode, and any number of other provocative souls. Boyers lives his ideas and makes them lively. This is not an academic book. It's a book that takes the pleasure of thinking seriously, and makes it palpable."

EDITORS' CORNER
New Works by Our
Advisory Editors

Peter Ho Davies, *The Fortunes*, a novel (September 2016, Houghton Mifflin Harcourt).

Gail Mazur, *Forbidden City* (April 2016, University of Chicago Press).

Alan Shapiro, *Life Pig*, poems (September 2016, University of Chicago Press).

Alan Shapiro, *That Self-forgetful Perfectly Useless Concentration*, essays (October 2016, University of Chicago Press).

Gerald Stern, *Divine Nothingness*, poems (May 2016, Norton).

Gerald Stern, *Insane Devotion*, essays (April 2016, Trinity University Press).

CONTRIBUTORS' NOTES

Peter Bichsel, born in 1935 in Lucerne, lives as a freelance author in Bellach. He has won numerous awards.

Lucy Biederman holds a doctorate in English from the University of Louisiana-Lafayette. She has written four chapbooks, and her essays and poems have appeared recently in *West Branch, Conjunctions, Pleiades, Denver Quarterly,* and *The Laurel Review.* Her website is lucybiederman.wordpress.com.

Chauna Craig is the author of the story collection *The Widow's Guide to Edible Mushrooms* (Queen's Ferry Press, 2016). Her stories and essays have appeared in *Prairie Schooner, Fourth Genre, SmokeLong Quarterly, Seattle Review,* and elsewhere. A Montana native, she now lives in western Pennsylvania and is professor of English at Indiana University of Pennsylvania.

John Cullen grew up in New Orleans and was educated at the universities of Virginia and Texas. He is the translator of many books from French, German, Italian, and Spanish. In 2010, his translation of Philippe Claudel's *Brodeck* won both the French-American Foundation Translation Prize and the Independent Foreign Fiction Prize. His most recent translations include Kamel Daoud's *The Meursault Investigation* (Other Press, 2015), Patrick Modiano's *Villa Triste* (Other Press, 2016), Chantal Thomas' *The Exchange of*

Princesses (Other Press, 2015), David Trueba's *Blitz* (Anagram, 2015), Juli Zeh's *Decompression* (Anchor, 2015), and Luigi Carletti's *Supernotes* (Nan A. Talese, 2016). He lives in upstate New York.

Kamel Daoud (born 1970) is an Algerian journalist and writer based in Oran. He writes a popular column for the French-language newspaper *Le Quotidien d'Oran* and has contributed articles and op-ed pieces to many other periodicals, including *Le Monde* and *The New York Times*. In 2013, following two short-story collections, he published his first novel, *Meursault, contre-enquête* (Barzakh Editions), which won several prizes, among them the Prix Goncourt du Premier Roman. An English translation, *The Meursault Investigation*, was published by Other Press in 2015.

British writer **Carys Davies** is the author of two collections of short stories, *Some New Ambush* (Salt Publishing, 2007) and *The Redemption of Galen Pike* (Salt Publishing, 2014), which won the 2015 Frank O'Connor International Short Story Award. She is also the recipient of the Royal Society of Literature's VS Pritchett Prize, the Society of Authors' Olive Cook Short Story Award, the Jerwood Fiction Uncovered Prize and a 2016/2017 Cullman Fellowship at the New York Public Library.

Lydia Davis is the author of *The Collected Stories of Lydia Davis* (Farrar, Straus & Giroux, 2009), a translation of Flaubert's *Madame*

Bovary (Viking Penguin, 2010), a chapbook entitled *The Cows* (Sarabande Press, 2011), and a poem entitled "Our Village" in *Two American Scenes* (New Directions, 2013). In 2013, she was awarded the Man Booker International Prize for Fiction, and her most recent collection of stories *Can't and Won't* was published in 2014 by Farrar, Straus & Giroux.

Kari Dickson grew up in Scotland, with a Norwegian mother. She read Scandinavian Studies at UCL and then went on to work in theater, before taking an MA in translation at the University of Surrey. Having worked initially as a commercial translator, including some years at the central bank of Norway, she now concentrates solely on literature. Her portfolio includes literary fiction, crime, nonfiction, and plays.

Viet Dinh was born in Vietnam and grew up in Colorado. He received his degrees from the Johns Hopkins University and the University of Houston and currently teaches at the University of Delaware. A recipient of a National Endowment for the Arts Fiction Fellowship, he is the author of *After Disasters* (Little A Books, 2016) and his short stories have appeared in the *O. Henry Prize Stories, Zoetrope: All-Story, Chicago Review, Fence, Threepenny Review, Five Points,* and other journals. He rarely gets seasick.

Emily Fox Gordon is the author of *Mockingbird Years: A Life In and Out of Therapy* (memoir) (Basic Books, 2001), *Are You Happy? A Childhood*

Remembered (memoir) (Riverhead Books, 2007), *It Will Come to Me* (novel) (Spiegel & Grau, 2009), and, most recently, *Book of Days: Personal Essays* (Spiegel & Grau, 2010). Her work has twice been reprinted in Pushcart Prize anthologies and once in *Best American Essays* (2014). With the support of a 2014 Guggenheim fellowship, she has been working on a second personal essay collection, *The View from Now*.

Amity Gaige is the author of three novels, *O My Darling* (Other Press, 2005), *The Folded World* (Random House Trade Paperbacks, 2009), and *Schroder (Twelve, 2013)*. A *New York Times* Notable Book, *Schroder* has been translated into eighteen languages and was shortlisted for UK's Folio Prize in 2014. Gaige is the winner of a Fulbright Fellowship, fellowships at the MacDowell and Yaddo colonies, a Baltic Writing Residency, and a Guggenheim Fellowship. She lives in Connecticut.

Georgi Gospodinov (born 1968) is a Bulgarian poet and writer. His debut novel, *Natural Novel* (1999), was published in twenty-three languages including English, German, French, Italian, Spanish, and, most recently, Icelandic. His second novel, *The Physics of Sorrow* (2012), won several national awards and was a finalist for six international prizes in Italy, Germany, and the US; among the prizes: Premio Strega Europeo, Premio Gregor von Rezzori, and the PEN Translation Prize. The novel has been published in the US (Open Letter Press, 2015), France,

Italy, Germany, the Netherlands, and elsewhere. His latest books are *The Invisible Crises* (Zhanet 45, 2013) (essays) and *And All Turned Moon* (Dalkey Archive Press, 2010) (short stories).

Cate Kennedy is an Australian writer who has published two short story collections, a novel, three poetry collections and a travel memoir. Her work has appeared in magazines and journals in Australia, the UK, Austria, and the US and translated into French, Spanish, German, and Mandarin. Cate is on the faculty of Pacific University's MFA program as a fiction advisor, and lives in rural Victoria, Australia. "Here is Where" is part of a longer work in progress, a novel entitled *Safekeeping* to be released by Scribe Publications.

Glyn Maxwell's *Drinks with Dead Poets* will be published in the UK by Oberon in September 2016. It is an expansion of his critical guidebook *On Poetry*, which was published by Harvard University Press in 2012. His poetry collections include *Pluto* (Picador, 2013), *The Nerve* (Mariner Books, 2004), *The Sugar Mile* (Mariner Books, 2006), and *One Thousand Nights and Counting* (Farrar, Straus and Giroux, 2012). He was Poetry Editor of *The New Republic* from 2000 to 2007, has had several plays staged in the UK and US, and has written fiction, libretti, and travelogue.

Melissa Pritchard is the recipient of the Flannery O'Connor and Carl Sandburg Awards, the Janet Heidinger Kafka Prize, a Barnes and

Noble Discover Great New Writers Award, and several Pushcart Prizes and O. Henry Awards. Her work has appeared in *The Paris Review, A Public Space, Ecotone, Conjunctions, Agni,* and *O, The Oprah Magazine,* among other places. Author of ten books, she is the 2016 Marguerite and Lamar Smith Fellow at the Carson McCullers Center for Writers and Musicians in Columbus, Georgia.

Angela Rodel is a literary translator living in Bulgaria. She received a 2014 NEA translation grant for Georgi Gospodinov's novel *The Physics of Sorrow* (Open Letter 2015). The novel was also short-listed for the 2016 Pen Translation Award. Six novels in her translation have been published by US and UK publishers. Her translations have appeared in literary magazines and anthologies, including *McSweeney's, Little Star,* Granta. org, *Two Lines, The White Review,* and *Words Without Borders.*

Viet Thanh Nguyen's novel *The Sympathizer* (Grove Press, 2015) won the Pulitzer Prize for Fiction, the Edgar Award for Best First Novel, the Andrew Carnegie Medal for Excellence in Fiction, and the First Novel Prize from the Center for Fiction. His other books are *Nothing Ever Dies: Vietnam and the Memory of War* (Harvard University Press, 2016) and *Race and Resistance: Literature and Politics in Asian America* (Oxford University Press, 2002). He is an associate professor of English and American Studies and Ethnicity at the University of Southern California.

Weike Wang earned her MFA in fiction from Boston University. She also holds degrees (BS and MS) from Harvard University. Her fiction has been published in *Smokelong Quarterly, Redivider, Alaska Quarterly Review,* and *Glimmer Train.* She currently lives in Boston and is working on a novel. She has a dog named Biscuit.

Gunnhild Øyehaug (born 1975) lives in Bergen, Norway. She debuted with the poetry collection *The Slave of the Blueberry* in 1998. Since then, she has published a short-story collection, *Knots* (Cappelen, 2004); an essay collection, *Chair and Ecstasy* (Cappelen, 2006); and two novels, *Wait, Blink* (Gyldendal, 2008) and *Undis Brekke* (Kolon Forlag, 2014). She has also written the screenplay for the movie *Women in Oversized Men's Shirts* (in cooperation with director Yngvild Sve Flikke), based on her novel *Wait, Blink,* which opened in cinemas in Norway in March 2015. Øyehaug has a degree in comparative literature and is a teacher at the Academy of Creative Writing in Bergen. She has received several awards for her writing, among others the prestigious Sult Prize (2009) and the Dobloug Prize (2009).

GUEST EDITOR POLICY

Ploughshares is published three times a year: mixed issues of poetry and prose in the spring and winter and a prose issue in the summer. The spring and summer issues are guest-edited by different writers of prominence, and winter issues are staff-edited. Guest editors are invited to solicit up to half of their issues, with the other half selected from unsolicited manuscripts screened for them by staff editors. This guest editor policy is designed to introduce readers to different literary circles and tastes, and to offer a fuller representation of the range and diversity of contemporary letters than would be possible with a single editorship. Yet, at the same time, we expect every issue to reflect our overall standards of literary excellence.

SUBMISSION POLICIES

We welcome unsolicited manuscripts from June 1 to January 15 (postmark dates). We also accept submissions online. Please see our website (pshares. org/submit) for more information and guidelines. All submissions postmarked from January 16 to May 31 will be recycled or returned unread. From March 1 to May 15, we accept submissions online for our Emerging Writer's Contest.

Our backlog is unpredictable, and staff editors ultimately have the responsibility of determining for which editor a work is most appropriate. If a manuscript is not timely for one issue, it will be considered for another. Unsolicited work sent directly to a guest editor's home or office will be ignored and discarded.

All mailed manuscripts and correspondence regarding submissions should be accompanied by a self-addressed, stamped envelope (s.a.s.e.) and email address. Expect three to five months for a decision. We now receive well over a thousand manuscripts a month.

For stories and essays that are significantly longer than 6,000 words, we are now accepting submissions for Ploughshares Solos, which will be published as e-books. Pieces for this series, which can be either fiction or nonfiction, can stretch to novella length and range from 7,500 to 25,000 words. The series is edited by Ladette Randolph, *Ploughshares* Editor-in-Chief.

Simultaneous submissions are amenable as long as they are indicated as such and we are notified immediately upon acceptance elsewhere. We do not reprint previously published work. Translations are welcome if permission has been granted. We cannot be responsible for delay, loss, or damage. Payment is upon publication: $25/ printed page, $50 minimum and $250 maximum per author, with two copies of the issue and a one-year subscription. For Ploughshares Solos, payment is $250 for long stories and $500 for work that is closer to a novella. The prize for our Emerging Writer's Contest is $1,000 for the winner in each genre: Fiction, Poetry, and Nonfiction.

PEN AMERICA

A JOURNAL FOR WRITERS AND READERS

ISSUE #19: HAUNTINGS

Featuring Conversations, Essays,
Fiction, Poetry & Art by
Tom Stoppard
Yusef Komunyakaa
Joyce Carol Oates
Mona Eltahawy
Laura Esquivel
Edward Snowden
Kimiko Hahn
& many others

www.PEN.org/journal